FUTURE
English for Results

INTRO

TESTS and TEST PREP
with **Exam**View® Assessment Suite

Jennifer Gaudet

Theresa Warren

Series Consultants

Beatriz B. Díaz

Ronna Magy

Federico Salas-Isnardi

PEARSON
Longman

Future Intro
English for Results
Tests and Test Prep

Pearson Education, 10 Bank Street, White Plains, NY 10606

Staff credits: The people who made up the *Future Intro Tests and Test Prep* team, representing editorial, production, design, and manufacturing, are: Nancy Flaggman, Irene Frankel, Shelley Gazes, Katherine Keyes, Liza Pleva, Barbara Sabella, and Julie Schmidt.

Cover design: Rhea Banker
Cover photo: Kathy Lamm/Getty Images
Text design: Barbara Sabella
Text composition: TSI Graphics
Text font: Minion Regular

Illustration credits: Steve Attoe: pp. 23 (item 1), 47 (item 2), 71 (item 2), 77, 81 (item 2), 84, 93, 96; Laurie Conley: pp. 7 (item 2), 28, 58, 92; Deborah Crowle: pp. 1 (item 1), 4; Brian Hughes: pp. 35, 38, 45, 54 (item 1), 78, 86; Luis Monteil: pp. 27; Chris Murphy: p. 57; Andy Myer: pp. 22, 63; Roberto Sadi: pp. 10, 73; Neil Stewart/NSV Productions: pp. 15 (item 1), 19, 26, 37, 87; Tinge Design Studio: pp. 43, 44; George Thompson: p. 88; Gary Torrisi: pp. 12, 47 (item 1), 50, 51, 71 (item 1), 75, 76; Anna Veltfort: pp. 7 (item 1), 70, 80, 81 (item 1); Wiliam Waitzman: pp. 15 (item 2), 39, 42, 59, 79, 85.

Photo credits: All original photography by David Mager. Page 1 (2A) Blend Images/Jupiterimages, (2B) Redchopsticks Collect/age footstock, (2C) Image Source/Jupiterimages; 6 BigStockPhoto.com; 14 KPG Mega/Shutterstock; 15 (item 3) (A) Payless Images/Shutterstock, (B) Rido/Fotolia, (C) .shock/Fotolia; 18 (1) Hillstreet Studios/Blend Images/Corbis, (2) .shock/Fotolia, (3) iofoto/Fotolia, (4) Wavebreak Media/Shutterstock; 30 Ronnie Kaufman/Corbis; 46 (L) Digital Vision Ltd./SuperStock, (R) Fotolia.com; 54 (2B) Robert Lerich/iStockphoto.com, (2C) Shutterstock; 60 (1) Index Stock Imagery, (2) Shutterstock, (3) Robert Lerich/iStockphoto.com, (4) Shutterstock; 61 (TL) Shutterstock, (TR) Shutterstock, (BL) Dorling Kindersley, (BR) Robert Lerich/iStockphoto.com; 62 Digital Vision/Getty Images; 63 (2A) Photofusion Picture Library/Alamy, (2B) Ingram Publishing/Getty Images, (2C) Mira/Alamy; 67 (1) John Eder/Getty Images, (2) Mark Gamba/Corbis, (4) Jack Hollingsworth/Corbis; 68 (L) Antonio Diaz/Fotolia, (R) I love images/Jupiterimages; 89 (1A) Shutterstock, (1B) Banana Stock/age footstock, (1C) Frank Herholdt/Getty Images, (2A) Shutterstock, (2B) Dynamic Graphics/Jupiterimages, (2C) Kurhan/Shutterstock

ISBN-13: 978-0-13-240929-2
ISBN-10: 0-13-240929-1

PEARSON LONGMAN ON THE WEB

Pearsonlongman.com offers online resources for teachers and students. Access our Companion Websites, our online catalog, and our local offices around the world.

Visit us at **www.pearsonlongman.com**.

Printed in the United States of America
6 17

Contents

Welcome to *Future Intro Tests and Test Prep.* This package (containing a book, audio CD, and e-CD) provides all the assessment tools you need:

- The **Test Prep** section at the beginning of the book contains test-taking strategy worksheets and a sample unit test.
- The **Printed Unit Tests** in the book test students' mastery of the content presented in the Student Book units. The audio CD accompanies these tests.
- The **Exam***View*® *Assessment Suite* on the e-CD offers a wealth of additional ways to assess students. Teachers can create their own unique tests or print or customize already prepared multilevel unit tests in addition to midterm and final tests.

TEST PREP

Many adult ESL students are unfamiliar with standardized tests. The Test Prep section contains reproducible worksheets that will prepare students for both the printed unit tests in this book and for any standardized tests they may have to take, such as the CASAS Life and Work Series. You will find the following worksheets on pages viii-xvi:

- How to Use an Answer Sheet
- Instructions for the Sample Unit Test
- Sample Unit Test (Listening, Grammar, and Life Skills sections)
- Answer Key and Audio Script for the Sample Unit Test (the teacher may choose not to distribute this to students)
- Standardized Tests: Practice Questions
- Test-Taking Strategies

You can distribute the worksheets to your class over a period of time (for example, one or two pages a week). Alternatively, you can wait until students are close to the time they will be tested or post-tested and then go over all the material in one session.

To administer the Sample Unit Test:

- Go over the Instructions for the Sample Unit Test worksheet with your class.
- Make copies of the Sample Unit Test and of the blank Answer Sheet on page 97. Distribute the copies to your students. Have them bubble in their test answers on the Answer Sheet.
- The audio for the sample listening questions can be found on the audio CD, Tracks 2–4. Play each track twice, pausing for 10 to 20 seconds between each play.
- Check answers using the Answer Key and the Audio Script for the Sample Unit Test on page xiv.

The Sample Unit Test (with the exception of the grammar section) is similar in format and content to the CASAS Reading and Listening Series tests, but not identical to them. The CASAS website (www.casas.org) offers additional information, such as practice test questions, that you may find useful.

PRINTED UNIT TESTS

There are 12 printed Unit Tests in this test booklet. They are designed to assess how well students have mastered the material presented in each unit of the Student Book. Each test contains the following sections:

- Listening
- Grammar
- Vocabulary
- Life Skills
- Reading

The Listening, Vocabulary, Life Skills, and Reading sections of the tests emulate the look and feel of the CASAS Life and Work Reading and Listening Series tests. All the sections use a multiple-choice format, modeling the format students will encounter in standardized tests.

Listening

The Listening section includes a variety of item types and is divided into three parts: **Listening I**, **Listening II**, and **Life Skills I**. (Life Skills I does not appear in every test.)

In the Listening I and Life Skills I sections, students listen to test items and look at the answer choices on the test page. The answer choices are usually pictures.

In Listening II, both the questions and the answer choices are on the audio CD. There are two types of questions. In the first type, students hear a statement or question and have to choose the appropriate response to that statement or question. In the second type, the students hear a short conversation and have to answer a comprehension question about that conversation.

The directions and the answer choices appear on the Listening II test page. This is different from the CASAS test, where students are not given answer choices to look at for these item types. In other words, students bubble in their answers on the answer sheet, but they do not see the questions or answer choices in print. If your students need extra support, give them the second page of the test, the Listening II page, when you distribute the test. But if you wish to emulate CASAS more closely, you should omit the second page of the test.

Grammar

Students are asked to complete short conversations that contain examples of the grammar points presented in the unit.

Vocabulary

Students identify pictures of vocabulary items that were presented in the vocabulary lesson(s) of the unit.

Life Skills

The Life Skills section may include both Listening and Reading items. In the Life Skills Listening section (Life Skills I), students look at three different pictures and listen to a sentence or conversation, and then choose the correct picture. In the Life Skills Reading section (either Life Skills I or Life Skills II), students read a brief text or look at pictures. Then they answer questions about the text or pictures.

Reading

Students read a short paragraph that reflects the grammar and themes covered in the unit and then answer comprehension questions about it.

Answer Keys and Audio Scripts

You will find an Answer Key and an Audio Script for each printed Unit Test at the back of this book. The Answer Key is an answer sheet with the correct answers for the test bubbled in. It also provides diagnostic information about each test question.

Administering and Scoring Printed Unit Tests

To administer a printed Unit Test:

- Find the test you want in this book and photocopy it.
- Decide whether or not you want students to look at the Listening II page as they take the test (see the Listening II section). Either include or omit the Listening II page when you distribute the test.
- Make copies of the blank Answer Sheet on page 97 and distribute them to your students. Ask students to bubble in their test answers on the Answer Sheet.
- Start with the Listening Section of the test. Locate the appropriate audio track on the audio CD. We recommend that you play each track twice, pausing for 10 to 20 seconds between each play. This will approximate how listening is presented on standardized tests.
- Each 25-item test is designed to take 25 to 30 minutes to administer.

To score a printed Unit Test:

- Collect your students' bubbled-in Answer Sheets.
- Locate the Answer Key for the test at the back of this book. To create a scoring mask, photocopy the Answer Key and punch a hole in each bubbled-in answer.

When you lay this scoring mask over a student's Answer Sheet, you can easily see if the student has bubbled in the correct answer. If the bubble is not filled in, then simply mark an *X* on the unmarked bubble with a colored pencil.

- Count the number of correctly bubbled in answers on the student's Answer Sheet. Each correct answer is worth three points. To calculate a percentage score for your students, multiply the number of correct answers by 3 to get the test score. Then multiply the test score by 4 and divide the answer by 3.

The Answer Key provides the objective that each item tests, along with the lesson and page number in the Student Book where the material was presented. If a student answers a particular item incorrectly, you will then know which competency the student has missed and/or in which lesson he or she may need further practice.

EXAM*VIEW*® ASSESSMENT SUITE

The **Exam***View*® *Assessment Suite* can be used either to supplement the printed Unit Tests or in place of them. With **Exam***View*, you can create or customize your own tests for students. Alternatively, you can choose to simply print out Unit, Midterm, or Final tests that have already been prepared for you and administer them to your class.

For detailed information on how to install the **Exam***View* software and use it to create, customize, and print out tests, please refer to the *TO THE TEACHER* PDF located on the *Future Intro* **Exam***View Assessment Suite* e-CD. The installation instructions in the back of this book will tell you how to find this document.

Exam*View* Unit Tests

The prepared **Exam***View* Unit Tests are designed to address the needs of multilevel classes. Each Unit Test is offered at three different levels: **pre-level**, **on-level**, and **above-level**. You can choose to divide your class into three different groups and to administer a different version of a test to each group simultaneously. You can also use different versions of a test to diagnose a student's level.

The **Exam***View* unit tests have the same general structure as the printed unit tests in the book, with a series of multiple choice questions that test listening, grammar, vocabulary, life skills, and reading skills. However, the **Exam***View* unit tests do not follow the CASAS testing format as closely as the printed unit tests do. Another difference is that there are two separate types of tests for each unit. The first is a Listening Test, in PDF format, and the second is an **Exam***View* Test, containing grammar, vocabulary, life skills, and reading items.

The Listening Tests are offered in PDF format to make them easier for teachers to administer. There are separate pre-level, on-level, and above level PDFs for each listening test. All three levels share the same audio. They also share the same basic structure: students listen to longer conversations (similar to the listenings in the Student Book) and then answer comprehension questions about them.

Meanwhile, grammar, vocabulary, life skills, and reading skills are tested in the **Exam***View* unit tests. There are separate pre-level, on-level, and above-level **Exam***View* tests for each unit. Again, all three levels share the same basic structure.

Exam*View* Midterm and Final Tests

The **Exam***View* Midterm and Final Tests are offered at on-level only in order to provide an objective, standardized way to assess all your students at the halfway point and at the end of the course. They have a total of 48 items each. The Midterm tests the content presented in Units 1–6 and the Final covers Units 7–12. As with the Unit Tests, the midterm and final listening tests are in PDF format, and the grammar, vocabulary, life skills, and reading items are in **Exam***View*.

Administering and Scoring Exam*View* Tests

To administer an **Exam***View* Test:

- You can administer **Exam***View* Tests via computer or simply print them out and distribute them to your students.
- If you want to administer a multilevel Unit Test, divide your class into pre-level, on-level, and above-level groups.

- Locate the appropriate PDFs and **Exam** *View* tests. For example, if you wanted to administer the pre-level version of the Unit 1 **Exam** *View* test, you would print out the pre-level Listening test PDF and the pre-level **Exam** *View* test for Unit 1. (Please refer to the *TO THE TEACHER* PDF on the **Exam** *View* e-CD for more information on how to select the PDFs or tests you need.)

- Distribute the tests to your students. (Note: the Answer Keys for the **Exam** *View* test print out automatically at the end of the test. Make sure you do not distribute the Answer Key to your students along with the test!)

- If you are printing out tests for your students, make copies of the blank answer sheet on page 97. Distribute two copies to each student. One copy is for the Listening Test, and the other copy is for the **Exam** *View* Test.

- Start with the Listening Test. Play the appropriate audio tracks for the test. Have students fill in the correct number of bubbles on the first answer sheet (usually, for six test items). Then collect the listening answer sheets.

- Next, administer the **Exam** *View* test for the unit. Have students bubble in the second answer sheet. Collect the answer sheets when students are finished.

- Allow 25-30 minutes for students to complete the Listening Test and the **Exam** *View* test for each unit. Allow 50-60 minutes for a midterm or final.

To score an **Exam** *View* Test:
- Collect your students' bubbled-in answer sheets.

- Locate the Answer Keys for the test. The Answer Keys and Audio Scripts for the Listening tests are in PDF format. For the Unit Tests, there is a pre-level Listening Answer Key, an on-level Listening Answer Key, and an above-level Listening Answer Key. Note that there is only one Audio Script for all three levels of the Unit Tests. The Answer Keys for the other tests will print out automatically at the end of each test, as noted above.

- Count the number of correctly bubbled in answers on each student's Answer Sheet. Score the **Exam** *View* Unit Tests as you would a printed Unit Test. For the 48-item Midterm or Final test, multiply the number of correct answers by 2, and add 4 free points to get a percentage score.

You will find detailed diagnostic information about each test item in the answer keys, including the following:
- Level of difficulty (DIF): Pre-level, On-level, or Above-level

- Reference (REF): Student Book level and unit being tested

- Learning objective (OBJ): the learning objective of the item (as found in the *Scope & Sequence*/Student Book unit lesson)

- National standard (NAT): the CASAS competency being tested, if applicable

- Skill (SKL): the skill being tested (listening, grammar, vocabulary, life skills, or reading)

As with the printed Unit Test Answer Keys, you can use this diagnostic information to determine the competencies and/or lessons in which your students need more practice.

HOW TO USE AN ANSWER SHEET

For many tests, you use an Answer Sheet to mark, or bubble in, your answers. You must use a #2 pencil. You do not mark your answers on the test. A machine may score your answers. The machine reads and records the pencil marks on the Answer Sheet.

First, you need to fill in some personal information on the Answer Sheet.

Here is an example of the Answer Sheet in this book:

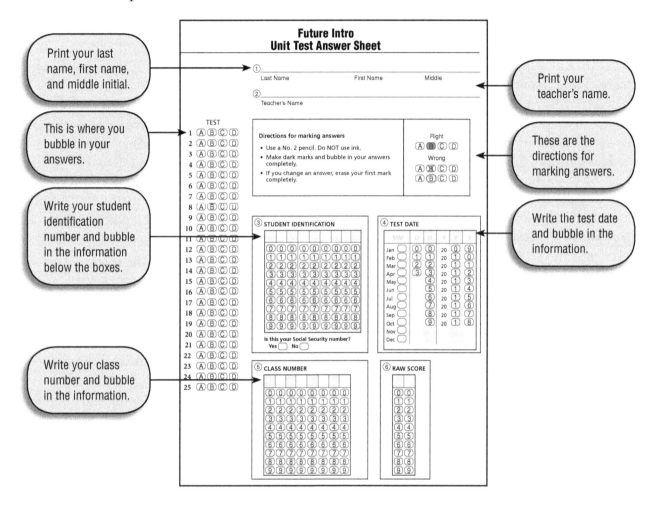

INSTRUCTIONS FOR THE SAMPLE UNIT TEST

This sample test is like the unit tests in this book. It has listening, grammar, and life skills questions. Follow the directions carefully.

Listening Section

All the questions in the listening section have three answer choices. You will hear each question two times. Here ar e examples of the three types of listening questions:

Example 1: You listen and choose the correct picture.
You will hear: *It's an eraser.*

| A | B | C |

correct answer: **A**

Example 2: You listen and choose the correct response to the statement or question.
You will hear: *Do you have a pen?*

    A. He's in the library.
    B. Turn off the light.
    C. Yes, I do.

correct answer: **C**

Example 3: You listen to a conversation and choose the correct answer to a question about it.
You will hear: **F:** *Where is the bookstore?*

               M: *It's next to the cafeteria.*

                 Where is the bookstore?

                 A. It's across from the cafeteria.
                 B. It's next to the cafeteria.
                 C. It's next to the computer lab.

correct answer: **B**

Grammar and Life Skills sections

The questions in the grammar section have three answer choices. You choose the correct answer to complete a conversation. The questions in the life skills section have four answer choices. You read or look at a picture and then answer a question about it.

SAMPLE UNIT TEST

🔊 LISTENING I

(Track 2) **Look at the pictures and listen. What is the correct answer: A, B, or C?**

1.

A

B

C

2.

A

B

C

💿 LISTENING II

(Track 3) Listen to the question and three answers.
What is the correct answer: A, B, or C?

3. A. Thanks.
    B. Open your book.
    C. No, I don't.

4. A. That's great!
    B. I ask the teacher questions.
    C. It's across from the men's room.

(Track 4) Listen to the conversation. Then listen to the question and
three answers. What is the correct answer: A, B, or C?

5. A. It's across from the cafeteria.
    B. It's next to the library.
    C. It's across from the library.

6. A. He's in the bookstore.
    B. He's in the office.
    C. He's in the teacher's room.

GRAMMAR

Complete each conversation. What is the correct answer: A, B, or C?

7. **A:** _____ a pen.

   B: OK.

    A. Don't

    B. Don't use

    C. Do not

8. **A:** How do you study English?

   B: _____ new words in my notebook.

    A. Write

    B. I write

    C. They write

LIFE SKILLS

Read. What is the correct answer: A, B, C, or D?

Vista Learning Center

PLEASE PRINT.

☐ Mr.
☑ Mrs.
☐ Miss
☐ Ms.

Lopez
Last Name

Mexico
Place of Birth

English 100
Class

Alexa
First Name

☑ Female   ☐ Male

Mr. Chen
Teacher

9. What is the student's last name?

   A. Mrs.

   B. Alexa

   C. Lopez

   D. Chen

10. Where is Alexa from?

    A. Vista Learning Center

    B. Mexico

    C. Ms. Cutler

    D. English 100

ANSWER KEY AND AUDIO SCRIPT FOR THE SAMPLE UNIT TEST

Answer Key

1. C	3. C	5. C	7. B	9. C
2. A	4. B	6. A	8. B	10. B

Audio Script

LISTENING I
(Track 2) Look at the pictures and listen.
What is the correct answer: A, B, or C?

1. Do you have a dictionary?
2. Put away your book.

LISTENING II
(Track 3) Listen to the question and three answers.
What is the correct answer: A, B, or C?

3. Do you have a piece of paper?
   A. Thanks.
   B. Open your book.
   C. No, I don't.

4. How do you study English?
   A. That's great!
   B. I ask the teacher questions.
   C. It's across from the men's room.

(Track 4) Listen to the conversation. Then listen to the question and three answers.
What is the correct answer: A, B, or C?

5. **F:** Where is the computer lab?
   M: It's across from the library.

   Where is the computer lab?
   A. It's across from the cafeteria.
   B. It's next to the library.
   C. It's across from the library.

6. **F:** Where is Pedro?
   M: He's in the bookstore.

   Where is Pedro?
   A. He's in the bookstore.
   B. He's in the office.
   C. He's in the teacher's room.

STANDARDIZED TESTS: PRACTICE QUESTIONS

Many standardized tests begin with a practice page. Here is an example of a practice page. Read through the questions below and make sure you understand how to answer them.

When you take a standardized test, find the practice page. It says *Practice*. Look for the practice answer box on the answer sheet. Use a pencil. Bubble in your answer. Ask the tester for help if you do not understand the directions. When the test begins, you are not allowed to talk. You cannot ask for or give help.

READING TEST

Practice 1

Here's a quarter.

PRACTICE

→ 1 (A) (B) (C) (D)
  2 (A) (B) (C) (D)

Practice 2

Sun.	Mon.	Tues.	Wed.	Thurs.	Fri.	Sat.
	computer class		English class			

When is the English class?

    A. It's on Monday.

    B. It's on Tuesday.

    C. It's on Wednesday.

    D. It's on Thursday.

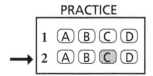

PRACTICE

  1 (A) (B) (C) (D)
→ 2 (A) (B) (C) (D)

TEST-TAKING STRATEGIES

Preparing to Take a Test

- Get a lot of sleep the night before the test.
- Eat a meal or snack before the test.
- Bring two sharpened #2 pencils.
- Bring a pencil eraser.
- Bring a ruler or a blank piece of paper.
- Arrive early to the testing room.
- Make sure you can easily see and hear the tester.
- Turn off your cell phone.
- Try to relax and do your best! Good luck!

Taking a Test

- As soon as you start a test section, look through the section to see how many questions there are.
- Don't spend too much time on any one question. If you don't know the answer, guess and then move on to the next item. You can circle the item number and come back to it at the end if you have time.
- For a listening section: Look at the answer choices for the question. Then listen to the directions and the question. Remember that for some questions, both questions and answer choices may be on the CD. You will hear the questions and the answer choices.
- For all other sections: Read the material. Read the question carefully. Read all the answer choices.
- Think: Which is the best answer? Look at the answer choices again. Eliminate answers you know are not correct.
- Choose the best answer.
- Make sure you mark your answer on the correct line on the answer sheet. Use a ruler to help you, or use a blank piece of paper to cover the lines below the line you are working on.
- Check each time that you bubble in the circle on the correct line for the question you are answering.
- Do not change the first answer you mark unless you are sure that it is wrong.
- Erase completely any answers you have changed. Fill in only ONE answer on each line. Erase all extra marks on your answer sheet.
- When you finish, if there is time, always recheck your answers.
- If you cannot answer many questions, it is OK. Raise your hand. Tell the tester. You may be excused from taking the rest of the test.

Unit 1 Test

🔘 LISTENING I

(Track 5) Look at the pictures and listen. What is the correct answer: A, B, or C?

1.

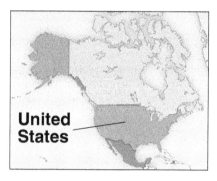

A	B	C

Canada   United States   Mexico

2.

    A   B   C

3.

KATHY	KATYA	CATIA
A	B	C

LISTENING II

(Track 6) Listen to the question and three answers. What is the correct answer: A, B, or C?

4. A. It's 213.
   B. It's 555-1212.
   C. I'm Hong.

5. A. That's right.
   B. I'm from Mexico.
   C. Hi, I'm Sam. Nice to meet you.

6. A. I'm from Peru.
   B. Hi, I'm Chen.
   C. Welcome!

(Track 7) Listen to the conversation. Then listen to the question and three answers. What is the correct answer: A, B, or C?

7. A. 96663
   B. 93336
   C. 93662

8. A. Salvador
   B. David
   C. Kalifa

9. A. Cambodia
   B. Korea
   C. Canada

GRAMMAR

Complete each conversation. What is the correct answer: A, B, or C?

10. **A:** _____ Tomas.
    B: You're right!

    A. You
    B. You're
    C. I

11. **A:** Manuel is a new student.
    B: Yes. _____ from Colombia.

    A. You are
    B. He
    C. He is

12. **A:** Where is Ms. Martin from?
    B: _____ from Canada.

    A. She's
    B. She
    C. Is

13. **A:** Who are they?
    B: Bao and Deng. They _____ my classmates.

    A. am
    B. is
    C. are

14. **A:** You are from Mexico.
    B: No. _____ from Venezuela.

    A. You are
    B. I
    C. I am

VOCABULARY

Read. What is the correct answer: A, B, C, or D?

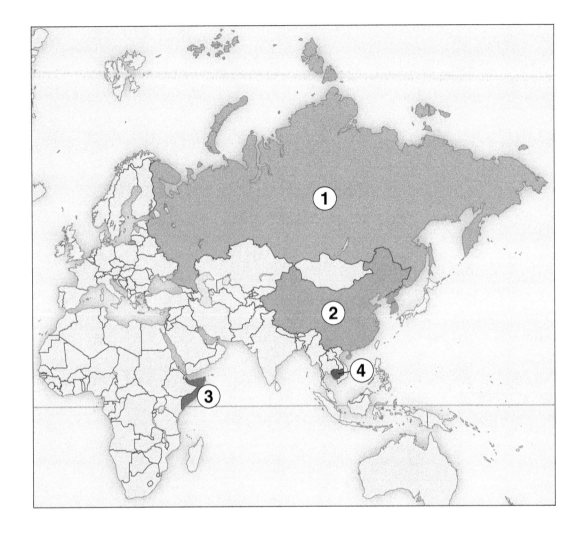

15. I'm from Cambodia.

    A. ①

    B. ②

    C. ③

    D. ④

16. She's from Somalia.

    A. ①

    B. ②

    C. ③

    D. ④

17. Chang is from China.

    A. ①

    B. ②

    C. ③

    D. ④

LIFE SKILLS

Read. What is the correct answer: A, B, C, or D?

Adult Education Center

Chen	Thi	Nguyen
First Name	Middle Name	Last Name

Telephone | 222 | – | 555-4567 | Place of Birth | Vietnam |

Area Code   Phone Number   Country

Student Identification Number   79012

18. What is the student's last name?
   A. Thi
   B. Nguyen
   C. Mayfield
   D. Vietnam

19. Where is the student from?
   A. Nguyen
   B. Chen
   C. Vietnam
   D. Adult Education Center

20. What is the student's phone number?
   A. 79012
   B. 555-4567
   C. 222
   D. 555

21. What is the student's student identification number?
   A. 79012
   B. 555-4567
   C. 222
   D. 555

READING

Read. What is the correct answer: A, B, C, or D?

My name is Larissa. I'm from Russia.
I'm a new student at Mayfield Adult School.
My classmates are from China and Mexico.
They are good students.
My English teacher is Mrs. Smith.
She's from the United States.
She's a good teacher.

22. Where is Larissa from?

A. the United States

B. Russia

C. China

D. Mexico

23. What is the name of Larissa's school?

A. Mrs. Smith

B. English teacher

C. Russia

D. Mayfield Adult School

24. Who are good students?

A. Mrs. Smith

B. Larissa

C. Larissa's classmates

D. Mayfield Adult School

25. Where is the teacher from?

A. the United States

B. Russia

C. China

D. Mexico

Unit 2 Test

LISTENING I

(Track 8) **Look at the pictures and listen. What is the correct answer: A, B, or C?**

1.

  A   **B**   **C**

2.

  A   **B**   **C**

🔘 LISTENING II

(Track 9) **Listen to the question and three answers.**
What is the correct answer: A, B, or C?

3. A. No, I don't.
    B. Thanks.
    C. OK.

4. A. Yes, I do.
    B. It's next to the office.
    C. He's in the cafeteria.

5. A. Yes, I do.
    B. I practice with my classmates.
    C. That's great!

(Track 10) **Listen to the conversation. Then listen to the question and three answers. What is the correct answer: A, B, or C?**

6. A. a pencil
    B. a pen
    C. an eraser

7. A. the woman
    B. Jack
    C. Mr. Wong

8. A. He asks the teacher questions.
    B. He writes in his notebook.
    C. He reads signs.

GRAMMAR

Complete each conversation. What is the correct answer: A, B, or C?

9. **A:** _____ your books.
   B: OK.

   A. Opens
   B. Open
   C. Don't

10. **A:** _____ the light.
    B: OK.

    A. Turn
    B. Don't turn
    C. Don't turn off

11. **A:** How do you study English?
    B: _____ signs on the street.

    A. Read
    B. They read
    C. I read

12. **A:** I use a pencil in class.
    B: Really? _____ a pen.

    A. They study
    B. I use
    C. I don't

Look at the picture. Complete the conversation.
What is the correct answer: A, B, or C?

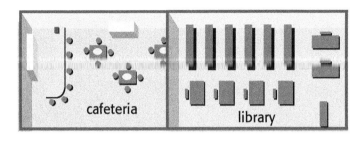

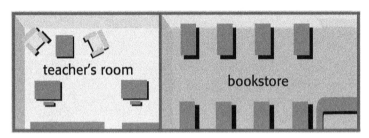

13. A: Where is the cafeteria?

    B: It's _____ the teacher's room.

      A. next to

      B. across

      C. across from

VOCABULARY

Read. What is the correct answer: A, B, C, or D?

14. Do you have a pencil?
   A. ①
   B. ②
   C. ③
   D. ④

15. Take out a piece of paper.
   A. ①
   B. ②
   C. ③
   D. ④

Read. What is the correct answer: A, B, C, or D?

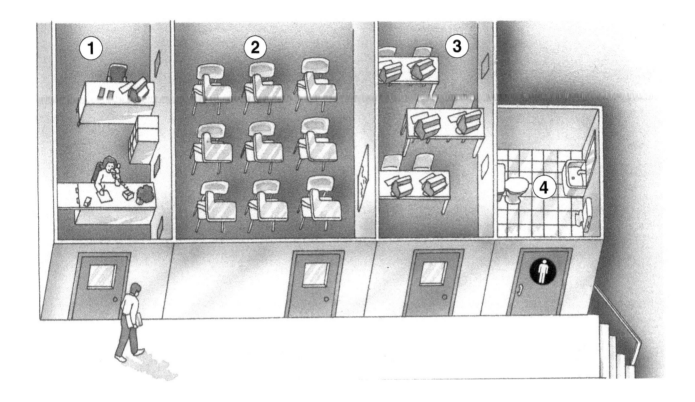

16. Where is the office?

    A. ①

    B. ②

    C. ③

    D. ④

17. Sergei is in the men's room.

    A. ①

    B. ②

    C. ③

    D. ④

LIFE SKILLS

Read. What is the correct answer: A, B, C, or D?

Vista Learning Center

PLEASE PRINT.

☑ Mr.
☐ Mrs.
☐ Miss
☐ Ms.

Canizares	Juan
Last Name	First Name

Ecuador	☐ Female ☑ Male
Place of Birth	

English 101	Ms. Cutler
Class	Teacher

18. What is the student's first name?
A. Mr.
B. Juan
C. Canizares
D. Cutler

19. What is the teacher's last name?
A. Mr.
B. Ms.
C. Canizares
D. Cutler

20. Where is the student from?
A. English 101
B. Ecuador
C. Vista Learning Center
D. male

21. What class is the student in?
A. English 101
B. Ecuador
C. Vista Learning Center
D. Ms. Cutler

READING

Read. What is the correct answer: A, B, C, or D?

My name is Jin Su. I'm a student. I'm from Korea.
In my country, teachers talk in class.
Students don't talk in class.
They write in their notebooks.
They don't ask the teacher questions.
They don't talk to their classmates.
In the United States, students ask the teacher many questions.

22. Who is Jin Su?

   A. a student from the United States

   B. a student from Korea

   C. a teacher from the United States

   D. a teacher from another country

23. What do teachers do in Korea?

   A. They talk in class.

   B. They don't talk in class.

   C. They talk to their classmates.

   D. They don't write in their notebooks.

24. What do students do in Korea?

   A. They talk in class.

   B. They write in their notebooks.

   C. They don't write in their notebooks.

   D. They ask the teacher questions.

25. Who asks many questions?

   A. students in the United States and Korea

   B. teachers and students in Korea

   C. students in the United States

   D. students in Korea

Unit 3 Test

💿 LISTENING I

(Track 11) Look at the pictures and listen. What is the correct answer: A, B, or C?

1.

A   B   C

2.

A   B   C

3.

A   B   C

LISTENING II

(Track 12) Listen to the question and three answers. What is the correct answer: A, B, or C?

4. A. That's early!

    B. I go to school from 1:00 to 4:00.

    C. You're really busy!

5. A. I work from Tuesday to Thursday.

    B. It's 8:30.

    C. That's late!

6. A. At 9:00.

    B. It's 4:30.

    C. It's from 2:00 to 4:00.

(Track 13) Listen to the conversation. Then listen to the question and three answers. What is the correct answer: A, B, or C?

7. A. from Monday to Friday

    B. on Monday and Tuesday

    C. on Monday and Thursday

8. A. It's from 9:30 to 10:00.

    B. It's at 8:30.

    C. It's at 10:00.

9. A. at 12:00 P.M.

    B. at 2:00 A.M.

    C. at 12:00 A.M.

GRAMMAR

Complete each conversation. What is the correct answer: A, B, or C?

10. **A:** Celi goes to class _____ 9:00 to 3:00.
    B: She's busy!

    A. to
    B. from
    C. at

11. **A:** When do you work?
    B: I work _____ Friday and Saturday.

    A. on
    B. at
    C. from

12. **A:** Fidel _____ breakfast at 6:00.
    B: That's early.

    A. work
    B. eats
    C. eat

13. **A:** Marco goes to school _____ 7:00 in the morning.
    B: That's early!

    A. on
    B. at
    C. from

14. **A:** Ivan _____ up at 9:30.
    B: That's late!

    A. goes
    B. get
    C. gets

VOCABULARY

Read. What is the correct answer: A, B, C, or D?

①

②

③

④

15. I take a shower at 7:15.

    A. ①

    B. ②

    C. ③

    D. ④

16. I get home at 4:30.

    A. ①

    B. ②

    C. ③

    D. ④

Read. What is the correct answer: A, B, C, or D?

① ②

17. What time is it on clock ①?

    A. 3:15

    B. 2:45

    C. 4:15

    D. 9:15

18. What time is it on clock ②?

    A. 10:05

    B. 11:05

    C. 12:55

    D. 1:05

LIFE SKILLS

Read. What is the correct answer: A, B, C, or D?

19. What is the number for **seventy-five**?

    A. 7

    B. 5

    C. 17

    D. 75

20. What is the word for **37**?

    A. three

    B. thirteen

    C. thirty-six

    D. thirty-seven

Read. What is the correct answer: A, B, C, or D?

Adolfa's Schedule

English Class 8:00 to 10:00

Break 10:00 to 10:30

21. What time is Adolfa's class?

    A. from 10:00 to 10:30

    B. from 8:00 to 10:00

    C. thirty minutes

    D. three hours

22. How long is Adolfa's break?

    A. from 10:30 to 12:00

    B. thirty hours

    C. thirty minutes

    D. 10:00

READING

Read. What is the correct answer: A, B, C, or D?

This is Kai.
He works Monday to Friday at Mario's Restaurant.
He gets up at 7:00 in the morning. He works from 9:00 to 5:00.
Kai goes to school after work.
He is in ESL class from 6:00 to 9:00.
He gets home at 9:15. He is very busy!

23. When does Kai work at Mario's Restaurant?

    A. from 9:00 to 5:00

    B. from 6:00 to 9:00

    C. at 7:00

    D. at 9:15

24. How long is Kai's ESL class?

    A. thirty minutes

    B. one hour

    C. three hours

    D. eight hours

25. When does Kai get home?

    A. at 7:00

    B. at 9:00

    C. at 6:00

    D. at 9:15

Unit 4 Test

✎ LISTENING I

(Track 14) Look at the pictures and listen. What is the correct answer: A, B, or C?

1.

A	B	C

2.

12/15/08	10/9/08	9/10/08
A	B	C

💿 LISTENING II

**(Track 15) Listen to the question and three answers.
What is the correct answer: A, B, or C?**

3. A. September 7, 2007.
   B. No, I don't.
   C. That's my mother.

4. A. That's nice.
   B. Yes. I have three daughters.
   C. My grandmother makes dinner.

5. A. April 12.
   B. I vacuum.
   C. I have two sisters.

**(Track 16) Listen to the conversations. Then listen to the question and three
answers. What is the correct answer: A, B, or C?**

6. A. October
   B. November
   C. August

7. A. Yes. He has two sons.
   B. No.
   C. Yes. He has one son and one daughter.

8. A. Tessa's mother
   B. Tessa's brother
   C. Tessa's sister

GRAMMAR

Complete each conversation. What is the correct answer: A, B, or C?

9. A: Do you have any _____?
B: No, I don't.

   A. sister
   B. brothers
   C. father

10. A: _____ cleans the house?
B: My father cleans the house.

   A. Who
   B. What time
   C. When

11. A: Diana is Carrie's _____.
B: Oh, really?

   A. daughters
   B. sisters
   C. mother

12. A: Who _____ out the garbage?
B: I take out the garbage.

   A. take
   B. takes
   C. do

13. A: Do you have any _____?
B: Yes, I have one daughter and two sons.

   A. children
   B. child
   C. parents

VOCABULARY

Read. What is the correct answer: A, B, C, or D?

October						
Sunday	Monday	Tuesday	Wednesday	Thursday	Friday	Saturday
	1 first	2 second	3 third	4 fourth	5 fifth	6 sixth

14. When is Anh's birthday?

    A. November fifth

    B. October sixth

    C. September sixth

    D. Sunday

Read. What is the correct answer: A, B, C, or D?

15. Who is Peichi's son?

    A. Yun-fat

    B. Bob

    C. Amy

    D. Enlai

16. Who is Peichi's grandmother?

    A. Yun-fat

    B. Jinghua

    C. Bob

    D. Enlai

Read. What is the correct answer: A, B, C, or D?

1

2

3

4

17. I clean the house.

    A. ①

    B. ②

    C. ③

    D. ④

LIFE SKILLS

Read. What is the correct answer: A, B, C, or D?

Adult Education Center

Adult
Education
Center

Name	Esteban	Pedro	Valencia
	First	Middle	Last

Date of Birth **3/1/48** Place of Birth **Mexico**

Class **ESL-2** Teacher **Mr. Black**

Class Schedule **Tuesday, Thursday** **9:00 A.M.–12:00 P.M.** **5**

Day/s   Time   Room

18. What is the student's middle name?

A. Valencia

B. Esteban

C. Pedro

D. Black

19. What is the student's date of birth?

A. January 3, 1948

B. March 1, 1948

C. February 1, 1948

D. January 3, 2008

20. When does the student go to class?

A. on Monday and Tuesday

B. on Tuesday

C. on Tuesday and Thursday

D. on Thursday

21. What time does the student's class end?

A. 9:00 A.M.

B. 12:00 P.M.

C. 9:00 A.M.–12:00 P.M.

D. 12:00 A.M.

READING

Read. What is the correct answer: A, B, C, or D?

My name is Ramiro Alvarez. This is my family.
We all do household chores.
My sister, Adriana, vacuums.
My father, Omar, takes out the garbage.
My wife, Rosa, makes dinner.
My mother, Miranda, does the laundry.
I wash the dishes.

22. Who vacuums?

  A. Ramiro's sister

  B. Ramiro's wife

  C. Ramiro's children

  D. Ramiro's mother

23. Who takes out the garbage?

  A. Ramiro's mother

  B. Ramiro's father

  C. Ramiro's son

  D. Ramiro's wife

24. Who is Ramiro's mother?

  A. Adriana

  B. Rosa

  C. Miranda

  D. Omar

25. What is Ramiro's household chore?

  A. He vacuums.

  B. He takes out the garbage.

  C. He does the laundry.

  D. He washes the dishes.

Unit 5 Test

🔵 LISTENING I

(Track 17) **Look at the pictures and listen. What is the correct answer: A, B, or C?**

1.

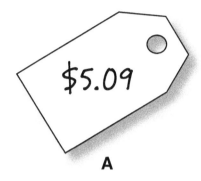

A

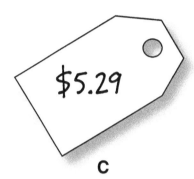

B   **C**

2.

A

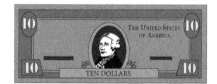

B   **C**

LISTENING II

(Track 18) **Listen to the question and three answers. What is the correct answer: A, B, or C?**

3. A. Thanks.

B. Yes, I have two tens.

C. Excuse me.

4. A. Yes, it is.

B. The toothpaste is $2.99.

C. Yes, I have three quarters.

5. A. They're $4.99.

B. Aisle 2.

C. How much are they?

(Track 19) **Listen to the conversation. Then listen to the question and three answers. What is the correct answer: A, B, or C?**

6. A. ten dollars

B. five dollars

C. one dollar

7. A. razor blades

B. soap

C. deodorant

8. A. $2.49

B. $3.49

C. $4.39

GRAMMAR

Complete each conversation. What is the correct answer: A, B, or C?

9. **A:** _____ the aspirin?
   B: Aisle 1.

   A. Where is
   B. Where
   C. Where are

10. **A:** _____ the batteries?
    B: Aisle 11.

    A. When are
    B. Where is
    C. Where are

11. **A:** Where are the _____?
    B: Aisle 7.

    A. lightbulb
    B. lightbulbs
    C. shampoo

12. **A:** _____ the soap?
    B: Aisle 12.

    A. Where are
    B. Where is
    C. How much

13. **A:** _____ the shaving cream?
    B: Aisle 4.

    A. Where
    B. Where is
    C. Where are

VOCABULARY

Read. What is the correct answer: A, B, C, or D?

(1)

(2)

(3)

(4)

14. I have a nickel.
    A. ①
    B. ②
    C. ③
    D. ④

15. Do you have change for a dollar?
    A. ①
    B. ②
    C. ③
    D. ④

Read. What is the correct answer: A, B, C, or D?

①

②

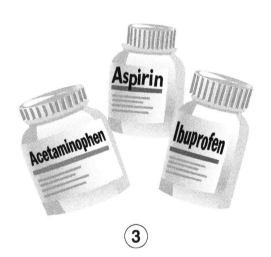

③

④

16. Is the deodorant on sale?

A. ①

B. ②

C. ③

D. ④

17. How much are the tissues?

A. ①

B. ②

C. ③

D. ④

LIFE SKILLS

Read. What is the correct answer: A, B, C, or D?

```
~~~~~~~~~~~~~~~~~~~~~~~~~~~~~~~~~~~~~

        Family Drugstore

          Date: 03/04/10

  1 Soap                    $3.99
  1 Paper towels             2.99
  1 Shaving cream            6.29




  Transaction Total:
  _____
  3 items     Subtotal    $13.27
              Tax           1.59
              Total       $14.86
  _____

  Paid by: Cash           $20.00
  Change                   $5.14

~~~~~~~~~~~~~~~~~~~~~~~~~~~~~~~~~~~~~
```

18. How much is the shaving cream?

    A. $3.99

    B. $2.99

    C. $6.29

    D. $13.27

19. How much is the tax?

    A. $13.27

    B. $1.59

    C. $14.86

    D. $5.14

Read. What is the correct answer: A, B, C, or D?

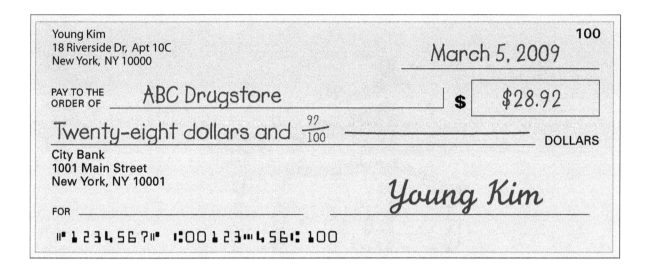

20. Who is writing this check?

    A. ABC Drugstore

    B. Riverside Dr.

    C. City Bank

    D. Young Kim

21. How much money is the check?

    A. $20.92

    B. $18

    C. $28.92

    D. 92 cents

READING

Read. What is the correct answer: A, B, C, or D?

Carla and Esteban are in the drugstore.
They need toilet paper and soap.
The soap is on aisle 7. It is $2.29.
The toilet paper is on aisle 6. It is on sale for $1.79!
Carla has only four quarters and two dimes.
Esteban pays for the items with a five.

22. What is on sale at the drugstore?

A. soap

B. toilet paper

C. toothpaste

D. soap and toilet paper

23. Where is the soap?

A. aisle 1

B. aisle 2

C. aisle 6

D. aisle 7

24. How much is the toilet paper?

A. $1.79

B. $2.20

C. $2.29

D. $5.00

25. How much money does Carla have?

A. $5.00

B. $1.00

C. $1.20

D. $1.79

NAME____________________

Unit 6 Test

LISTENING I

***(Track 20)* Look at the pictures and listen. What is the correct answer: A, B, or C?**

1.

A

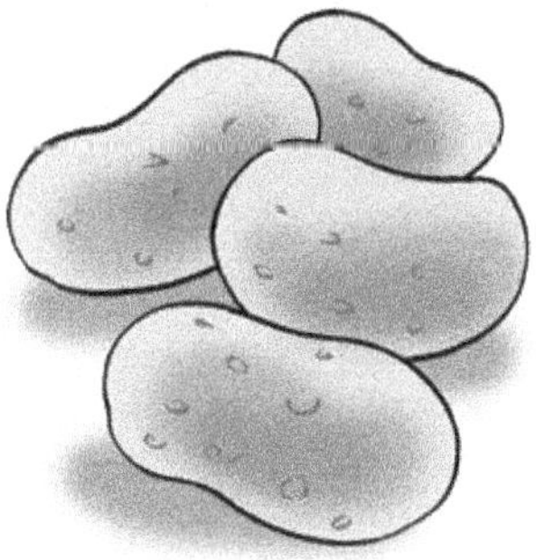

B

C

2.

A

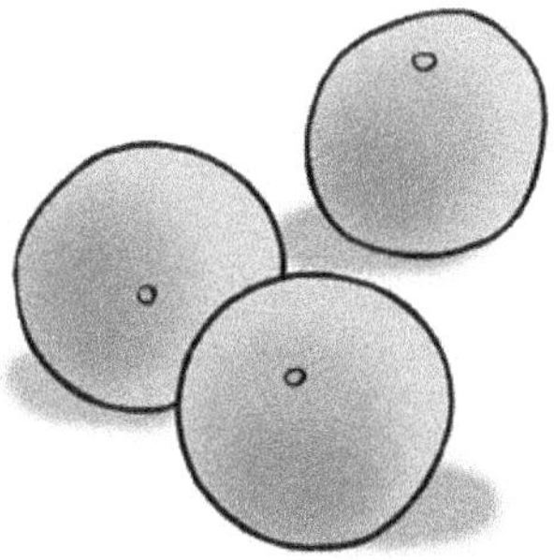

B

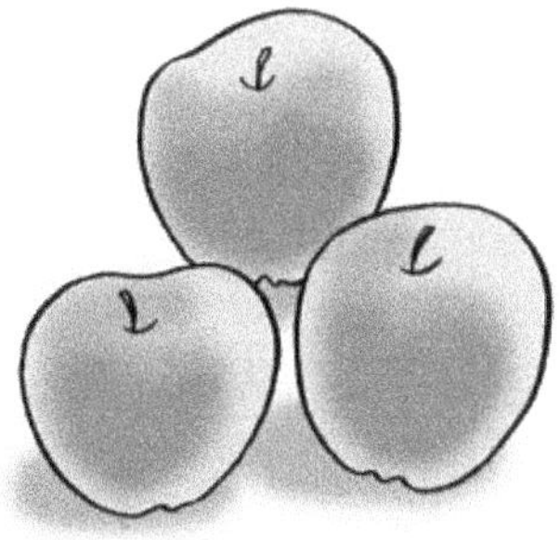

C

 **LISTENING II**

***(Track 21)* Listen to the question and three answers. What is the correct answer: A, B, or C?**

3. A. Yes.

    B. I'm at the store.

    C. I don't like mushrooms.

4. A. No, thanks.

    B. A loaf of bread.

    C. Yes, I like carrots.

***(Track 22)* Listen to the conversations. Then listen to the question and three answers. What is the correct answer: A, B, or C?**

5. A. tea and pancakes

    B. iced tea and cake

    C. coffee and cake

6. A. pears

    B. grapes and pears

    C. grapes

7. A. a green salad

    B. a baked potato

    C. a fruit salad

8. A. potatoes

    B. tomatoes and onions

    C. avocados and tomatoes

GRAMMAR

Complete each conversation. What is the correct answer: A, B, or C?

9. A: Do you like vegetables?

    B: Yes. We _____ potatoes.

       A. like

       B. likes

       C. don't like

10. A: Amir and Zarah _____ peaches.

    B: Really?

       A. doesn't like

       B. likes

       C. don't like

11. A: Does your wife like onions?

    B: Yes. She _____ mushrooms.

       A. like

       B. don't like

       C. doesn't like

12. A: My daughter _____ apples.

    B: Really? My son doesn't like apples.

       A. don't like

       B. likes

       C. like

13. A: I _____ ground beef. What about you?

    B: I like fish.

       A. like

       B. doesn't like

       C. likes

VOCABULARY

Read. What is the correct answer: A, B, C, or D?

1

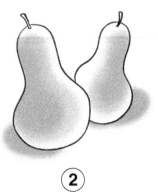

3

2

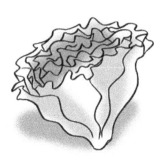

4

14. My mother likes pears.

    A. ①

    B. ②

    C. ③

    D. ④

15. Rodolfo doesn't like lettuce.

    A. ①

    B. ②

    C. ③

    D. ④

Read. What is the correct answer: A, B, C, or D?

16. What does Ying eat for lunch?

   A. a hamburger, French fries, and iced tea

   B. a hamburger, French fries, and milk

   C. a fish sandwich, a baked potato, and iced tea

   D. a chicken sandwich, rice, and juice

17. What does Ted want?

   A. tea and cake

   B. coffee and cake

   C. tea and ice cream

   D. coffee and ice cream

LIFE SKILLS

Read. What is the correct answer: A, B, C, or D?

WHAT ANH NEEDS

WHAT CARLOS NEEDS

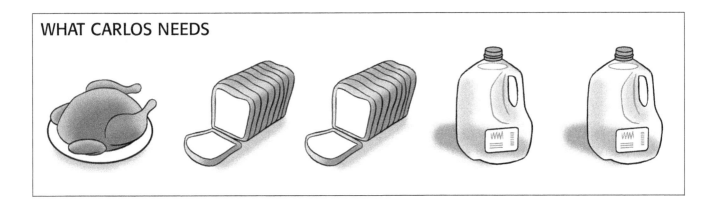

18. What does Anh need from the store?

    A. a box of cereal and a dozen eggs

    B. two boxes of cereal, two cans of soup, and two dozen eggs

    C. two boxes of cereal, two cans of soup, and one dozen eggs

    D. two boxes of cereal, one can of soup, and one dozen eggs

19. What does Carlos need from the store?

    A. a chicken, a loaf of bread, and a gallon of milk

    B. two chickens, two loaves of bread, and two gallons of milk

    C. a chicken, two loaves of bread, and a gallon of milk

    D. a chicken, two loaves of bread, and two gallons of milk

Read. What is the correct answer: A, B, C, or D?

Loaf of bread
$2.15
Buy one, get one free

One dozen eggs
$1.10

One bag of rice
$4.00

One gallon of milk
$1.99

20. How much are two loaves of bread?

   A. $2.15

   B. $4.30

   C. $1.10

   D. $4.00

21. How much are two bags of rice?

   A. $2.15

   B. $4.00

   C. $4.30

   D. $8.00

22. How much is a gallon of milk?

   A. $1.99

   B. $2.15

   C. $3.10

   D. $4.00

READING

Read. What is the correct answer: A, B, C, or D?

> Freddy is at the store.
> Tomatoes are on sale for $2 a pound. Lettuce is on sale, too. It's $1.15 a pound.
> Freddy has a shopping list. There are no vegetables on the list.
> Freddy calls his a girlfriend, Maria.
> Maria wants hamburgers and a green salad for dinner.
> Freddy buys tomatoes, lettuce, a loaf of bread, and ground beef.

23. What is on sale?

   A. tomatoes and bread

   B. tomatoes and lettuce

   C. ground beef and lettuce

   D. tomatoes and ground beef

24. What does Maria want for dinner?

   A. hamburgers and French fries

   B. chicken sandwiches and a green salad

   C. hamburgers and a green salad

   D. hamburgers and a fruit salad

25. What does Freddy buy?

   A. hamburgers and fruit salad

   B. ground beef, bread, and lettuce

   C. ground beef, a loaf of bread, tomatoes, and lettuce

   D. tomatoes, lettuce, and two loaves of bread

Unit 7 Test

🖸 LISTENING I

(Track 23) **Look at the pictures and listen. What is the correct answer: A, B, or C?**

1.

A   B   C

2.

A   B   C

LISTENING II

(Track 24) Listen to the question and three answers. What is the correct answer: A, B, or C?

3. A. I have a new apartment.
    B. It's 155 North Blakc Street.
    C. It has one bedroom.

4. A. It's $775 a month.
    B. There's a modern bathroom.
    C. There's an apartment for rent on my block.

5. A. It's 1440 Carnation Street.
    B. No, there aren't.
    C. There is a small kitchen.

(Track 25) Listen to the conversation. Then listen to the question and three answers. What is the correct answer: A, B, or C?

6. A. a dishwasher
    B. a washing machine
    C. a dryer

7. A. a living room, a kitchen, and one bedroom
    B. a dining room, a kitchen, and two bedrooms
    C. a living room, a kitchen, and two bedrooms

8. A. $895 a month
    B. $795 a month
    C. $805 a month

GRAMMAR

Complete each conversation. What is the correct answer: A, B, or C?

9. **A:** What's the apartment like?
   B: _____ two bedrooms.

   A. There is
   B. There are
   C. There isn't

10. **A:** I have a new apartment. _____ a sunny kitchen.
    B: It sounds great!

    A. There is
    B. There are
    C. Is there

11. **A:** _____ two bathrooms?
    B: Yes, there are.

    A. Is there
    B. There are
    C. Are there

12. **A:** Are there sofas in the living room?
    B: No, _____.

    A. there aren't
    B. there isn't
    C. there are

13. **A:** Is there a refrigerator?
    B: Yes, _____.

    A. there isn't
    B. there are
    C. there is

VOCABULARY

Read. What is the correct answer: A, B, C, or D?

14. There is one bathroom.

    A. ①

    B. ②

    C. ③

    D. ④

15. Is there a dining room?

    A. ①

    B. ②

    C. ③

    D. ④

Read. What is the correct answer: A, B, C, or D?

16. There is a dresser.

    A. ①

    B. ②

    C. ③

    D. ④

17. Is there a table?

    A. ①

    B. ②

    C. ③

    D. ④

LIFE SKILLS

Read. What is the correct answer: A, B, C, or D?

Ms. Paula James
1980 Garden St.
Dallas, TX 75254

Mr. and Mrs. Eli Perlas
2387 W. Water Rd.
Los Angeles, CA 90003

18. Who is the letter from?

A. Dallas

B. Ms. Paula James

C. Los Angeles

D. Mr. and Mrs. Perlas

19. What is the return address?

A. 2387 W. Water Rd.

B. Los Angeles, CA

C. 1980 Garden St., Dallas, TX 75254

D. Ms. Paula James

20. What does "Rd." mean?

A. apartment

B. street

C. road

D. avenue

21. What is Paula's ZIP code?

A. TX

B. 75254

C. 2387

D. 90003

READING

Read. What is the correct answer: A, B, C, or D?

Phuong and her parents need an apartment. There is an apartment on Brookhurst Street. The rent is $1,050 a month. There is a sunny living room, a kitchen, two bedrooms, and a bathroom. There is a dishwasher. There isn't a washing machine. Phuong and her parents like the apartment.

22. Who needs an apartment?

   A. Phuong and her children

   B. Phuong's parents

   C. Phuong and her parents

   D. Phuong's husband

23. How much is the rent?

   A. It's $500 a month.

   B. It's $1,050 a month.

   C. It's $105 a month.

   D. It's $1,050 a year.

24. What is the apartment like?

   A. There are three bedrooms.

   B. There isn't a kitchen.

   C. There are two bathrooms.

   D. There is a sunny living room.

25. Are there any appliances in the apartment?

   A. No, there aren't.

   B. Yes, there are. There is a washing machine and a dishwasher.

   C. Yes, there are. There is a washing machine. There isn't a dishwasher.

   D. Yes, there are. There is a dishwasher. There isn't a washing machine.

Unit 8 Test

🔊 LISTENING I

(Track 26) Look at the pictures and listen. What is the correct answer: A, B, or C?

1.

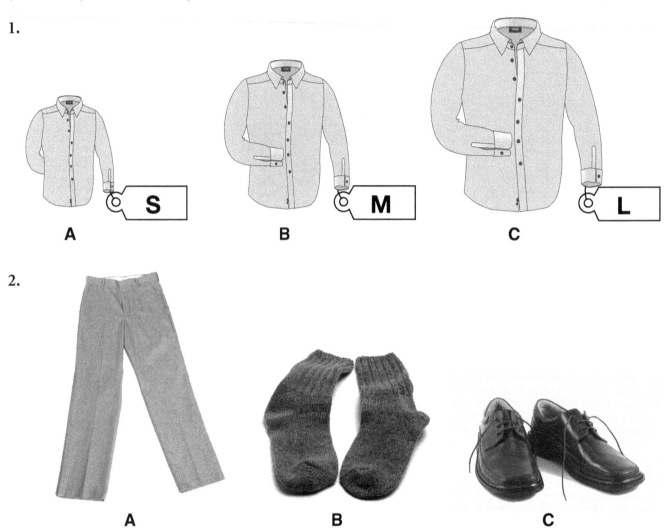

A   B   C

2.

A   B   C

🔘 LISTENING II

(Track 27) **Listen to the question and three answers.
What is the correct answer: A, B, or C?**

3. A. No, I'm sorry, we don't.
   B. OK, I need new shoes.
   C. Can I help you?

4. A. OK. Thanks.
   B. It is too big.
   C. Yes. She's over there. She's wearing a purple shirt.

5. A. What's the problem?
   B. He's wearing a green jacket.
   C. Here's my receipt.

(Track 28) **Listen to the conversation. Then listen to the question and three answers. What is the correct answer: A, B, or C?**

6. A. a large shirt
   B. a small jacket
   C. a large jacket

7. A. His shirt is too long.
   B. His T-shirt is too short.
   C. His shirt is too small.

GRAMMAR

Complete each conversation. What is the correct answer: A, B, or C?

8. **A:** Do you have _____ blouse in a size 5?
   B: Yes, we do.

   A. these
   B. those
   C. this

9. **A:** I need to return _____ pants.
   B: OK. What's the problem?

   A. these
   B. that
   C. this

10. **A:** Is Manny over there?
    B: Yes. He's wearing a _____ shirt.

    A. pants
    B. green
    C. that

11. **A:** Do you have this blouse in a large?
    B: No, but we have _____ blouse in a medium.

    A. those
    B. that
    C. these

**Look at the picture. Complete the sentence.
What is the correct answer: A, B, or C?**

Adam

12. A: Is Adam here?
 B: Yes. He's wearing _____.

    A. sweater and gray pants
    B. gray sweater and gray
    C. a gray sweater and gray pants

VOCABULARY

Read. What is the correct answer: A, B, C, or D?

① 1

② 2

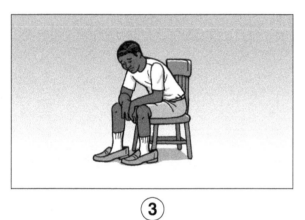

③ 3

④ 4

13. They are too short.

   A. ①

   B. ②

   C. ③

   D. ④

14. It is too long.

   A. ①

   B. ②

   C. ③

   D. ④

Read. What is the correct answer: A, B, C, or D?

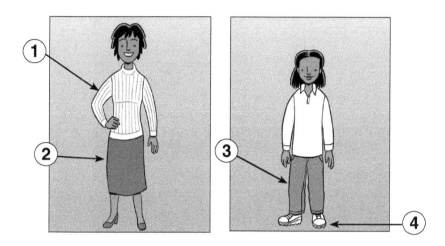

15. She is wearing sneakers.

    A. ①

    B. ②

    C. ③

    D. ④

16. She is wearing a skirt.

    A. ①

    B. ②

    C. ③

    D. ④

Read. What is the correct answer: A, B, C, or D?

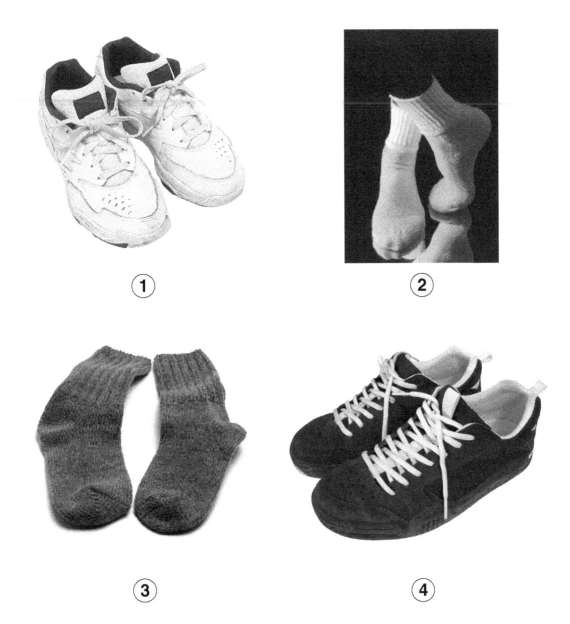

1

2

3

4

17. I need black sneakers.

 A. ①

 B. ②

 C. ③

 D. ④

18. Do you have gray socks?

 A. ①

 B. ②

 C. ③

 D. ④

LIFE SKILLS

Read. What is the correct answer: A, B, C, or D?

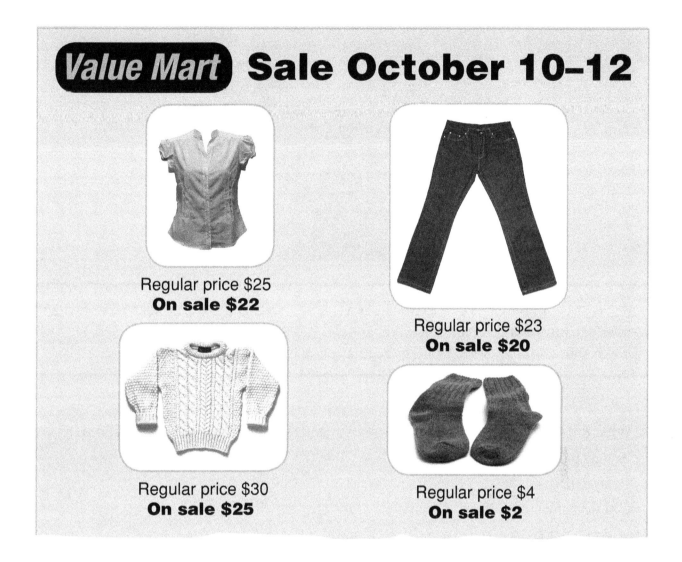

Value Mart Sale October 10–12

Regular price $25
On sale $22

Regular price $23
On sale $20

Regular price $30
On sale $25

Regular price $4
On sale $2

19. When is the sale?
   A. October 1–2
   B. October 1–12
   C. October 10
   D. October 10–12

20. What is the regular price of the jeans?
   A. $25
   B. $22
   C. $23
   D. $20

21. What is the sale price of the sweater?
   A. $30
   B. $25
   C. $22
   D. $20

22. How much can you save on socks?
   A. $1
   B. $2
   C. $3
   D. $4

READING

Read. What is the correct answer: A, B, C, or D?

Alex is at Clothes Mart. Clothes Mart has a sale this weekend. Alex needs a new shirt and shoes. He buys a large green shirt. It is on sale. It is $15. The regular price is $20. He buys brown shoes, too. They are $30. The regular price is $45. Alex is happy.

23. What does Alex need?

A. new pants

B. large pants

C. a new shirt

D. green pants

24. What size shirt does Alex buy?

A. XS

B. S

C. M

D. L

25. How much are the brown shoes this weekend?

A. $15

B. $20

C. $30

D. $45

Unit 9 Test

🔘 LISTENING I

(Track 29) **Look at the pictures and listen. What is the correct answer: A, B, or C?**

1.

| A | B | C |

2.

| A | B | C |

🖸 LISTENING II

(Track 30) **Listen to the question and three answers.**
What is the correct answer: A, B, or C?

3. A. Bye.
   B. Yes. I'm exercising.
   C. No problem.

4. A. How often?
   B. I play the guitar.
   C. No problem. Bye.

5. A. No, he isn't.
   B. I'll see him later.
   C. He does homework.

(Track 31) **Listen to the conversation. Then listen to the question and three answers. What is the correct answer: A, B, or C?**

6. A. She uses e-mail.
   B. She goes to the movies.
   C. She listens to music.

7. A. She's talking on the phone.
   B. She's visiting friends.
   C. She's watching TV.

8. A. He's working on the computer.
   B. He's looking for something.
   C. He's taking a break.

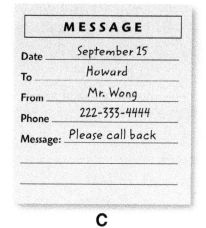LIFE SKILLS I

(Track 32) **Look at the pictures and listen. What is the correct answer: A, B, or C?**

9.

MESSAGE		
Date	September 15	
To	Mr. Smith	
From	Mr. Wong	
Phone	222-333-4444	
Message:	Please call back	

A

MESSAGE		
Date	September 15	
To	Mr. Wong	
From	Howard Smith	
Phone	222-333-4444	
Message:	Please call back	

B

MESSAGE		
Date	September 15	
To	Howard	
From	Mr. Wong	
Phone	222-333-4444	
Message:	Please call back	

C

10.

MESSAGE		
Date	September 15	
To	Dr. Flaggman	
From	Mrs. Grant	
Phone	222-453-5555	
Message:	She's not coming to her appointment today. Her daughter is sick.	

A

MESSAGE		
Date	September 15	
To	Dr. Grant	
From	Mrs. Flaggman	
Phone	222-453-5555	
Message:	She's coming to her appointment today.	

B

MESSAGE		
Date	September 15	
To	Mrs. Grant	
From	Dr. Flaggman	
Phone	222-453-5555	
Message:	She's not coming to her appointment today. She is sick.	

C

GRAMMAR

Complete each conversation. What is the correct answer: A, B, or C?

11. **A:** What are you doing?

 B: I _____ the car.

 A. am washing
 B. is washing
 C. are washing

12. **A:** Is Deng doing homework?

 B: Yes, _____.

 A. he isn't
 B. they are
 C. he is

13. **A:** _____ laundry?

 B: Yes, they are.

 A. Are they doing
 B. Are they
 C. They are doing

14. **A:** Is Kira taking a break?

 B: No, _____.

 A. she isn't
 B. she is
 C. isn't taking a break

15. **A:** Is Bella counting money?

 B: No. She _____ money. She's taking orders.

 A. is not
 B. 's not counting
 C. not counting

VOCABULARY

Read. What is the correct answer: A, B, C, or D?

①

②

③

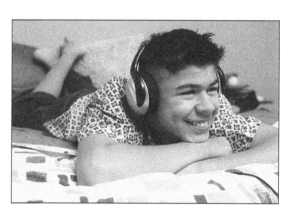

④

16. I watch TV three times a week.

   A. ①

   B. ②

   C. ③

   D. ④

17. I'm listening to music.

   A. ①

   B. ②

   C. ③

   D. ④

Read. What is the correct answer: A, B, C, or D?

Ted

Leonard

18. What is Ted doing?

    A. He's walking the dog.

    B. He's exercising.

    C. He's taking out the garbage.

    D. He's answering the phone.

19. What is Leonard doing?

    A. He's using e-mail.

    B. He's driving a truck.

    C. He's washing the car.

    D. He's playing the guitar.

LIFE SKILLS II

Read. What is the correct answer: A, B, C, or D?

Message	
For Mrs. Steiner	**Date** January 6
Caller Irene Franklin	**Phone** 555-555-0071
Message She isn't coming to work today. She is sick.	

20. Who is the message for?

   A. Mr. Franklin

   B. Mrs. Steiner

   C. Irene

   D. Franklin

21. What is the message?

   A. Irene is coming to work today.

   B. Mrs. Steiner isn't coming to work today.

   C. Irene is sick today. She isn't coming to work.

   D. Mrs. Steiner is coming to her appointment today.

READING

Read. What is the correct answer: A, B, C, or D?

Pedro and Ernesto work in a restaurant. Today they are very busy. Pedro is making pizzas. He isn't answering the phone. Ernesto is answering the phone. He is taking orders for pizza. He is also helping customers. They aren't taking a break now. They are working hard. They take a break twice a day.

22. Where are Pedro and Ernesto?

   A. at home

   B. in a store

   C. in a restaurant

   D. outside

23. What is Pedro doing?

   A. He is taking orders.

   B. He is talking on the phone.

   C. He is helping customers.

   D. He is making pizzas.

24. What is Ernesto doing?

   A. He is taking orders.

   B. He isn't talking on the phone.

   C. He isn't helping customers.

   D. He is making pizzas.

25. How often do Pedro and Ernesto take a break?

   A. every day

   B. twice a day

   C. three times a day

   D. They don't take breaks.

Unit 10 Test

🔵 LISTENING I

(Track 33) Look at the pictures and listen. What is the correct answer: A, B, or C?

1.

A

B   C

2.

A

B   C

💿 LISTENING II

(Track 34) Listen to the question and three answers.
What is the correct answer: A, B, or C?

3. A. Take the subway.
   B. On the corner of First Street and Main Street.
   C. I'm going to my English class.

4. A. Yes. It's across from the library.
   B. How do you get to school?
   C. Thanks a lot!

5. A. Go straight.
   B. He walks.
   C. Turn left at White Street.

(Track 35) Listen to the conversation. Then listen to the question and three
answers. What is the correct answer: A, B, or C?

6. A. to the subway
   B. to the school
   C. to the ATM

7. A. They take a taxi.
   B. They take a train.
   C. They take a ferry.

💿 LIFE SKILLS I

(Track 36) **Look at the pictures and listen. What is the correct answer: A, B, or C?**

8.

A   **B**   **C**

GRAMMAR

Complete each conversation. What is the correct answer: A, B, or C?

9. **A:** The fire station is _____ the hospital and the DMV.
   B: OK, thanks.

   A. across from
   B. between
   C. across

10. **A:** Excuse me. Where is the library?
    B: It's _____ City Hall.

    A. between
    B. in
    C. across from

11. **A:** Is the ATM _____ the park and the courthouse?
    B: Yes, it is.

    A. from
    B. between
    C. across

Look at the map. Then complete each conversation.
What is the correct answer: A, B, or C?

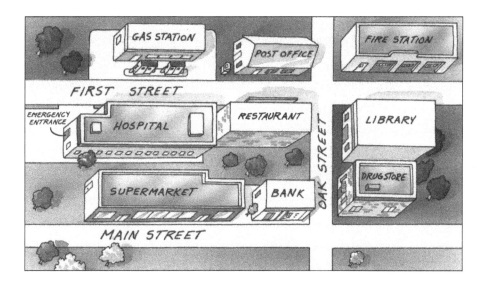

12. **A:** Is there a bank near here?

    B: Yes. It's _____ the drugstore.

      A. on

      B. between

      C. across from

13. **A:** Where's the post office?

    B: It's _____ the gas station and the fire station.

      A. across from

      B. between

      C. across

VOCABULARY

Read. What is the correct answer: A, B, C, or D?

(1)

(2)

(3)

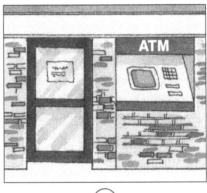

(4)

14. The drugstore is between First Street
and Park Avenue.

A. ①

B. ②

C. ③

D. ④

15. Where is the gas station?

A. ①

B. ②

C. ③

D. ④

Read. What is the correct answer: A, B, C, or D?

①

②

③

④

16. I carpool to school.

   A. ①

   B. ②

   C. ③

   D. ④

17. Gina takes the bus.

   A. ①

   B. ②

   C. ③

   D. ④

LIFE SKILLS II
Read. What is the correct answer: A, B, C, or D?

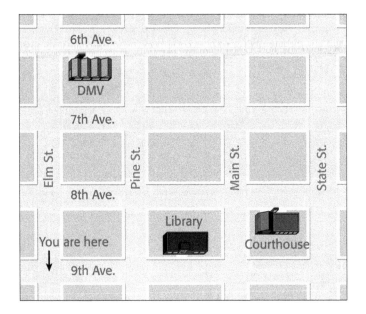

18. Where's the DMV?

A. Go straight on Elm Street for three blocks. Then turn right on 6th Avenue.

B. Go straight on 6th Avenue for three blocks. Then turn right on State Street.

C. Go straight on Elm Street for one block. Then turn left on 8th Avenue.

D. Turn right on Elm Street. Then turn left on Pine Street.

19. Is the courthouse near here?

A. Yes. It's on 7th Avenue.

B. Yes. Go straight on 9th Avenue for three blocks. Then turn left on State Street.

C. Yes. Go straight on 9th Avenue for one block. Then turn left on Pine Street.

D. It's across from the DMV.

20. Where is the library?

A. Turn right on Elm Street. Go straight for two blocks.

B. Go straight on Elm Street for two blocks. Turn right on 7th Avenue.

C. It's between the DMV and the courthouse.

D. Go straight on 9th Avenue for one block.

Read. What is the correct answer: A, B, C, or D?

①

②

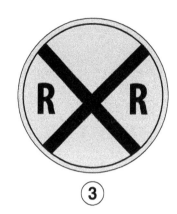

③

21. What does sign ② mean?

   A. Go this way.

   B. Stop.

   C. Don't park here.

   D. Walk now.

22. What does sign ③ mean?

   A. Don't turn left.

   B. Drive 25 miles per hour.

   C. Don't make a U-turn.

   D. Watch for a train crossing this street.

READING

Read. What is the correct answer: A, B, C, or D?

Hassan walks to English class on Monday and Tuesday. He goes straight on Bank Street for two blocks. Then he turns right on First Street. He goes straight for three blocks. Then Hassan turns left on Main Street. His school is on Main Street. It's between the park and the supermarket.

23. Where does Hassan go on Monday and Tuesday?

A. to the park

B. to the supermarket

C. to school

D. to a bank

24. How many blocks does Hassan walk on First Street?

A. one

B. two

C. three

D. four

25. Where is Hassan's school?

A. on Bank Street

B. across from the park

C. on First Street

D. between the park and the supermarket

Unit 11 Test

LISTENING I

(Track 37) Look at the pictures and listen. What is the correct answer: A, B, or C?

1.

 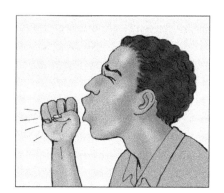 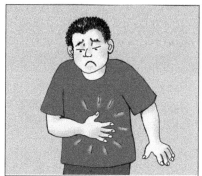

| A | B | C |

2.

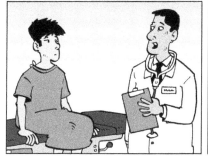 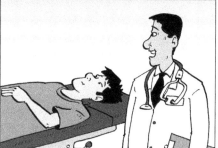 

| A | B | C |

 **LISTENING II**

(Track 38) **Listen to the question and three answers.
What is the correct answer: A, B, or C?**

3.   A. You should drink lots of liquids.
     B. Look straight ahead.
     C. My knee hurts.

4.   A. My head hurts.
     B. Yes, she can.
     C. I have an appointment.

5.   A. I have a stomachache.
     B. Get well soon!
     C. Open your mouth.

(Track 39) **Listen to the conversation. Then listen to the question and three
answers. What is the correct answer: A, B, or C?**

6.   A. She's across the street.
     B. She's on Main Street.
     C. She's on Garden Street.

7.   A. a lot of rest
     B. a lot of liquids
     C. aspirin

8.   A. There was a car accident.
     B. The woman's father has a backache.
     C. The woman's father is having a heart attack.

GRAMMAR

Complete each conversation. What is the correct answer: A, B, or C?

9. **A:** I have a headache.
   B: You _____ two aspirin.

   A. should
   B. take
   C. should take

10. **A:** I have the flu.
    B: You _____ home from work.

    A. should
    B. should stay
    C. stay

11. **A:** Dr. Troy, my chest hurts today.
    B: OK. _____ in.

    A. Breathe
    B. Breathes
    C. You breathe

12. **A:** I have a sore throat.
    B: OK. _____ your mouth.

    A. Opens
    B. Open
    C. We open

13. **A:** My son has a fever.
    B: He _____ a lot of liquids.

    A. should
    B. drink
    C. should drink

VOCABULARY

Read. What is the correct answer: A, B, C, or D?

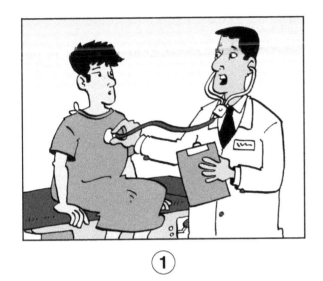

①

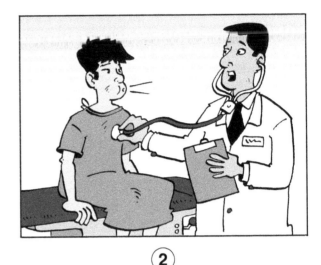

②

③

④

14. Step on the scale.

   A. ①

   B. ②

   C. ③

   D. ④

15. Breathe in.

   A. ①

   B. ②

   C. ③

   D. ④

Read. What is the correct answer: A, B, C, or D?

16. My shoulder hurts.

    A. ①

    B. ②

    C. ③

    D. ④

17. My knee hurts.

    A. ①

    B. ②

    C. ③

    D. ④

LIFE SKILLS

Read. What is the correct answer: A, B, C, or D?

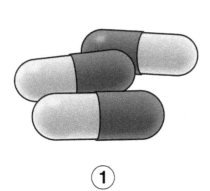

1

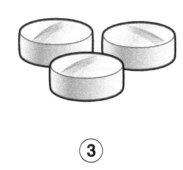

2

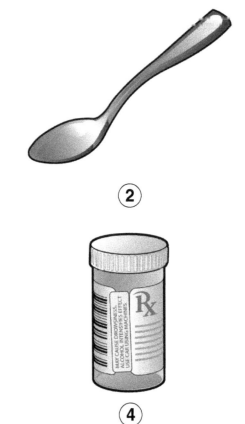

3

4

18. Please take three capsules every day.

    A. ①

    B. ②

    C. ③

    D. ④

19. She takes prescription medicine every six hours.

    A. ①

    B. ②

    C. ③

    D. ④

20. You should take three tablets every day for fever.

    A. ①

    B. ②

    C. ③

    D. ④

Read. What is the correct answer: A, B, C, or D?

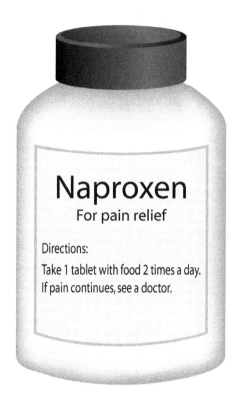

21. This medicine is for _____.
    A. pain
    B. fever
    C. cough
    D. sore throat

22. Celia's knee hurts. She should take _____.
    A. 2 tablets one time a day
    B. 2 tablets two times an hour
    C. 1 tablet two times a day
    D. 2 tablets with food two times a day

READING

Read. What is the correct answer: A, B, C, or D?

Tony has a headache and a stomachache. He has an appointment with the doctor. Tony sits on the table. He breathes in and breathes out. The doctor checks him. She says Tony should get a lot of rest. He should stay home from work. She gives Tony prescription medicine. Tony should take two capsules of the medicine every day.

23. Tony's _____ hurts.

A. chest

B. shoulder

C. arm

D. head

24. Tony should _____.

A. go to work

B. drink lots of liquids

C. get a lot of rest

D. take two tablets

25. The doctor gives Tony _____.

A. cough syrup

B. capsules

C. tablets

D. two teaspoons of medicine

Unit 12 Test

🔘 LISTENING I

(Track 40) Look at the pictures and listen. What is the correct answer: A, B, or C?

1.

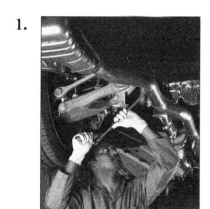  

| A | B | C |

2.

| A | B | C |

LISTENING II

(Track 41) **Listen to the question and three answers.**
What is the correct answer: A, B, or C?

3. A. Let's get coffee.

    B. I can't. I have to go to work.

    C. I'm a construction worker.

4. A. That's Brenda.

    B. She works at Family Restaurant.

    C. She's a nurse.

5. A. I use a computer.

    B. I'd like to apply for a job.

    C. I work at Longview Hospital.

(Track 42) **Listen to the conversation. Then listen to the question and three**
answers. What is the correct answer: A, B, or C?

6. A. She works in a café.

    B. She's a teacher's assistant.

    C. She's a sales assistant.

7. A. at a supermarket

    B. at a drugstore

    C. at a restaurant

8. A. build houses

    B. help sick people

    C. fix cars

GRAMMAR

Complete each conversation. What is the correct answer: A, B, or C?

9. **A:** Where _____ Jack work?
   B: He works at a factory.

   A. is
   B. do
   C. does

10. **A:** Can your sons build houses?
    B: No, they _____.

    A. don't
    B. can
    C. can't

11. **A:** Where _____ you work?
    B: I work at Centennial School.

    A. have
    B. do
    C. does

12. **A:** Can Karen use a cash register?
    B: Yes, she _____.

    A. uses
    B. can't
    C. can

13. **A:** _____ help sick people?
    B: Yes, they can.

    A. Aksana and Zamila can
    B. Can Aksana and Zamila
    C. Does Aksana

VOCABULARY

Read. What is the correct answer: A, B, C, or D?

①

②

Hello. 你好

③

④

14. I can speak two languages.

   A. ①

   B. ②

   C. ③

   D. ④

15. I can use office machines.

   A. ①

   B. ②

   C. ③

   D. ④

Read. What is the correct answer: A, B, C, or D?

①

②

③

④

16. What does the person in Picture ① do?

    A. She is a housekeeper.

    B. She is a construction worker.

    C. She is a custodian.

    D. She is a homemaker.

17. What does the person in Picture ② do?

    A. He is a mechanic.

    B. He is a security guard.

    C. He is a painter.

    D. He is a teacher's assistant.

LIFE SKILLS

Read. What is the correct answer: A, B, C, or D?

HELP WANTED

Federal Bank

Security Guard
Part-time Monday–Friday, 1:00–6:00 P.M.
Experience required
Call 555-666-2121 for interview appointment

18. The bank needs _____.

  A. a housekeeper

  B. a custodian

  C. a security guard

  D. an office assistant

19. The person needs to _____.

  A. have computer skills

  B. have experience

  C. speak two languages

  D. work full time

20. To apply for the job, the person should _____.

  A. call 555-666-2121 for an interview

  B. call 555-555-2121 for an interview

  C. go to the bank and apply in person

  D. send an e-mail

Read. What is the correct answer: A, B, C, or D?

City Diner
Cashiers Needed
F/T M–F 12:00–7:00

No exp. req. Will train.

Apply in person.

21. This job ad is for a _____.

   A. waitress

   B. cashier

   C. housekeeper

   D. cook

22. The person needs to work _____.

   A. part-time

   B. weekdays and weekends

   C. Monday and Friday

   D. full-time

READING

Read. What is the correct answer: A, B, C, or D?

Luis works at Memorial Hospital. He works full-time, Monday to Friday. He has ten years of experience. He is a nurse. He helps sick people. He can speak two languages. He can't use computers. Luis takes a computer class on the weekend.

23. Where does Luis work?

    A. at a computer company

    B. at a hospital

    C. Monday to Friday

    D. in a computer class

24. What can Luis do?

    A. He can speak three languages.

    B. He can use a computer.

    C. He can help sick people.

    D. He can use office machines.

25. What does Luis do on the weekend?

    A. He works at the hospital.

    B. He takes an English class.

    C. He takes a nursing class.

    D. He takes a computer class.

Future Intro
Unit Test Answer Sheet

① _____

Last Name   First Name   Middle

② _____

Teacher's Name

TEST

1 Ⓐ Ⓑ Ⓒ Ⓓ
2 Ⓐ Ⓑ Ⓒ Ⓓ
3 Ⓐ Ⓑ Ⓒ Ⓓ
4 Ⓐ Ⓑ Ⓒ Ⓓ
5 Ⓐ Ⓑ Ⓒ Ⓓ
6 Ⓐ Ⓑ Ⓒ Ⓓ
7 Ⓐ Ⓑ Ⓒ Ⓓ
8 Ⓐ Ⓑ Ⓒ Ⓓ
9 Ⓐ Ⓑ Ⓒ Ⓓ
10 Ⓐ Ⓑ Ⓒ Ⓓ
11 Ⓐ Ⓑ Ⓒ Ⓓ
12 Ⓐ Ⓑ Ⓒ Ⓓ
13 Ⓐ Ⓑ Ⓒ Ⓓ
14 Ⓐ Ⓑ Ⓒ Ⓓ
15 Ⓐ Ⓑ Ⓒ Ⓓ
16 Ⓐ Ⓑ Ⓒ Ⓓ
17 Ⓐ Ⓑ Ⓒ Ⓓ
18 Ⓐ Ⓑ Ⓒ Ⓓ
19 Ⓐ Ⓑ Ⓒ Ⓓ
20 Ⓐ Ⓑ Ⓒ Ⓓ
21 Ⓐ Ⓑ Ⓒ Ⓓ
22 Ⓐ Ⓑ Ⓒ Ⓓ
23 Ⓐ Ⓑ Ⓒ Ⓓ
24 Ⓐ Ⓑ Ⓒ Ⓓ
25 Ⓐ Ⓑ Ⓒ Ⓓ

Directions for marking answers

- Use a No. 2 pencil. Do NOT use ink.
- Make dark marks and bubble in your answers completely.
- If you change an answer, erase your first mark completely.

Right
Ⓐ ⬛ Ⓒ Ⓓ

Wrong
Ⓐ ⊠ Ⓒ Ⓓ
Ⓐ Ⓑ Ⓒ Ⓓ

③ STUDENT IDENTIFICATION

(Columns of bubbles numbered 0–9)

Is this your Social Security number?
Yes ☐   No ☐

④ TEST DATE

MM	D	D	Y	Y	Y

Jan Feb Mar Apr May Jun Jul Aug Sep Oct Nov Dec

(Date bubbles: 0–3 for first D; 0–9 for second D; 20; 0–1; 0–9)

⑤ CLASS NUMBER

(Columns of bubbles numbered 0–9)

⑥ RAW SCORE

(Columns of bubbles numbered 0–9)

Unit 1 Test Answer Key

ANSWERS	LESSON/PAGE	OBJECTIVE
1 (A) B C D	1/p. 9	Say where someone is from
2 A B (C) D	1/p. 9	Introduce someone
3 A (B) C D	2/p. 11	Spell first and last names
4 A (B) C D	3/p. 13	Say and write numbers
5 A B (C) D	4/p. 14	Introduce someone
6 (A) B C D	1/p. 9	Say where someone is from
7 A B (C) D	3/p. 12	Say and write numbers
8 A (B) C D	4/p. 14	Introduce someone
9 A (B) C D	6/p. 18	Say where someone is from
10 A (B) C D	6/p. 19	*You are, we are, they are*
11 A B (C) D	5/p. 17	*He is, she is*
12 (A) B C D	5/p. 17	*He is, she is*
13 A B (C) D	6/p. 19	*You are, we are, they are*
14 A B (C) D	4/p. 15	*I am, you are*
15 A B C (D)	1/p. 8	Identify countries
16 A B (C) D	1/p. 8	Identify countries
17 A (B) C D	1/p. 8	Identify countries
18 A (B) C D	7/p. 20	Fill out a form
19 A B (C) D	7/p. 20	Fill out a form
20 A (B) C D	7/p. 20	Fill out a form
21 (A) B C D	7/p. 20	Fill out a form
22 A (B) C D		Read for details
23 A B C (D)		Read for details
24 A B (C) D		Read for details
25 (A) B C D		Read for details

Please see reverse for test audio script.

Unit 1 Test Audio Script

LISTENING I
(Track 5) Page 1. Look at the pictures and listen. What is the correct answer: A, B, or C?

1. I'm from Canada.
2. Hello. My name is John.
3. I spell my first name K-A-T-Y-A.

LISTENING II
(Track 6) Page 2. Listen to the question and three answers.
What is the correct answer: A, B, or C?

4. What's your phone number?
   A. It's 213.
   B. It's 555-1212.
   C. I'm Hong.

5. Hello. My name is Maria.
   A. That's right.
   B. I'm from Mexico.
   C. Hi, I'm Sam. Nice to meet you.

6. Where are you from?
   A. I'm from Peru.
   B. Hi, I'm Chen.
   C. Welcome!

(Track 7) Page 2. Listen to the conversation. Then listen to the question and three answers.
What is the correct answer: A, B, or C?

7. **F:** What is your student ID number?
   M: 93662.

   What is his student ID number?
   A. 96663
   B. 93336
   C. 93662

8. **M:** Hi, my name is David. I'm from El Salvador.
   F: Hi! I'm Kalifa. I'm from Somalia.

   What's the man's name?
   A. Salvador
   B. David
   C. Kalifa

9. **F:** Where are they from?
   M: They're from Korea.

   Where are the people from?
   A. Cambodia
   B. Korea
   C. Canada

Unit 2 Test Answer Key

ANSWERS	LESSON/PAGE	OBJECTIVE
1 Ⓐ Ⓑ **Ⓒ** Ⓓ	2/p. 30	Follow classroom instructions
2 Ⓐ **Ⓑ** Ⓒ Ⓓ	3/p. 33	Identify places in a school
3 **Ⓐ** Ⓑ Ⓒ Ⓓ	1/p. 29	Ask for classroom objects
4 Ⓐ Ⓑ **Ⓒ** Ⓓ	3/p. 33	Identify places in a school
5 Ⓐ **Ⓑ** Ⓒ Ⓓ	6/p. 38	Talk about study skills
6 Ⓐ Ⓑ **Ⓒ** Ⓓ	1/p. 29	Ask for classroom objects
7 Ⓐ **Ⓑ** Ⓒ Ⓓ	3/p. 33	Identify places in a school
8 **Ⓐ** Ⓑ Ⓒ Ⓓ	6/p. 38	Talk about study skills
9 Ⓐ **Ⓑ** Ⓒ Ⓓ	2/p. 31	Imperatives
10 Ⓐ Ⓑ **Ⓒ** Ⓓ	2/p. 31	Imperatives
11 Ⓐ **Ⓑ** Ⓒ Ⓓ	6/p. 39	Simple present: *I, you, we, they*
12 Ⓐ **Ⓑ** Ⓒ Ⓓ	6/p. 39	Simple present: *I, you, we, they*
13 Ⓐ **Ⓑ** Ⓒ Ⓓ	4/p. 34	Prepositions of place
14 Ⓐ Ⓑ Ⓒ **Ⓓ**	1/p. 28	Identify classroom objects
15 Ⓐ **Ⓑ** Ⓒ Ⓓ	1/p. 28	Identify classroom objects
16 **Ⓐ** Ⓑ Ⓒ Ⓓ	4/p. 34	Identify places in a school
17 Ⓐ Ⓑ Ⓒ **Ⓓ**	4/p. 34	Identify places in a school
18 Ⓐ **Ⓑ** Ⓒ Ⓓ	5/p. 36	Fill out a form
19 Ⓐ Ⓑ Ⓒ **Ⓓ**	5/p. 36	Fill out a form
20 Ⓐ **Ⓑ** Ⓒ Ⓓ	5/p. 36	Fill out a form
21 **Ⓐ** Ⓑ Ⓒ Ⓓ	5/p. 36	Fill out a form
22 Ⓐ **Ⓑ** Ⓒ Ⓓ		Read for details
23 **Ⓐ** Ⓑ Ⓒ Ⓓ		Read for details
24 **Ⓐ** Ⓑ Ⓒ Ⓓ		Read for details
25 Ⓐ Ⓑ **Ⓒ** Ⓓ		Read for details

Please see reverse for test audio script.

Unit 2 Test Audio Script

LISTENING I
(Track 8) Page 7. Look at the pictures and listen. What is the correct answer: A, B, or C?

1. Turn off the light.
2. He's in the bookstore.

LISTENING II
(Track 9) Page 8. Listen to the question and three answers.
What is the correct answer: A, B, or C?

3. Do you have a dictionary?
   A. No, I don't.
   B. Thanks.
   C. OK.

4. Where is Juan?
   A. Yes, I do.
   B. It's next to the office.
   C. He's in the cafeteria.

5. How do you study English?
   A. Yes, I do.
   B. I practice with my classmates.
   C. That's great!

(Track 10) Page 8. Listen to the conversation. Then listen to the question and three answers.
What is the correct answer: A, B, or C?

6. **M:** Do you have an eraser?
   F: Yes, I do. Here you go.

   What does the man want?
   A. a pencil
   B. a pen
   C. an eraser

7. **F:** Hi, Jack. Where is Mr. Wong?
   M: He's in the bookstore.

   Who is in the bookstore?
   A. the woman
   B. Jack
   C. Mr. Wong

8. **F:** How do you study English?
   M: I ask the teacher questions.

   How does the man study English?
   A. He asks the teacher questions.
   B. He writes in his notebook.
   C. He reads signs.

Unit 3 Test Answer Key

ANSWERS	LESSON/PAGE	OBJECTIVE
1 Ⓐ Ⓑ **Ⓒ** Ⓓ	2/p. 48	Talk about class schedules
2 Ⓐ Ⓑ **Ⓒ** Ⓓ	1/p. 47	Say the time
3 Ⓐ **Ⓑ** Ⓒ Ⓓ	3/p. 51	Talk about daily activities
4 Ⓐ **Ⓑ** Ⓒ Ⓓ	4/p. 52	Talk about class schedules
5 Ⓐ Ⓑ **Ⓒ** Ⓓ	3/p. 51	Talk about daily activities
6 Ⓐ **Ⓑ** Ⓒ Ⓓ	1/p. 47	Say the time
7 Ⓐ **Ⓑ** Ⓒ Ⓓ	4/p. 52	Talk about days of the week
8 **Ⓐ** Ⓑ Ⓒ Ⓓ	2/p. 48	Talk about class schedules
9 **Ⓐ** Ⓑ Ⓒ Ⓓ	2/p. 48	Talk about class schedules
10 **Ⓐ** Ⓑ Ⓒ Ⓓ	2/p. 49	*From/to, at*
11 **Ⓐ** Ⓑ Ⓒ Ⓓ	4/p. 53	*From/to, on*
12 Ⓐ **Ⓑ** Ⓒ Ⓓ	3/p. 51	Third person singular
13 Ⓐ **Ⓑ** Ⓒ Ⓓ	2/p. 49	*From/to, at*
14 Ⓐ Ⓑ **Ⓒ** Ⓓ	3/p. 51	Third person singular
15 Ⓐ **Ⓑ** Ⓒ Ⓓ	3/p. 50	Identify daily activities
16 Ⓐ Ⓑ Ⓒ **Ⓓ**	3/p. 50	Identify daily activities
17 Ⓐ **Ⓑ** Ⓒ Ⓓ	1/p. 46	Identify clock time
18 Ⓐ **Ⓑ** Ⓒ Ⓓ	1/p. 46	Identify clock time
19 Ⓐ Ⓑ Ⓒ **Ⓓ**	5/p. 54	Read and write numbers
20 Ⓐ Ⓑ Ⓒ **Ⓓ**	5/p. 54	Read and write numbers
21 Ⓐ **Ⓑ** Ⓒ Ⓓ	5/p. 54	Interpret schedules
22 Ⓐ Ⓑ **Ⓒ** Ⓓ	5/p. 54	Interpret schedules
23 **Ⓐ** Ⓑ Ⓒ Ⓓ		Read for details
24 Ⓐ Ⓑ **Ⓒ** Ⓓ		Read for details
25 Ⓐ Ⓑ Ⓒ **Ⓓ**		Read for details

Please see reverse for test audio script.

Unit 3 Test Audio Script

(Track 11) Page 15. Look at the pictures and listen.
What is the correct answer: A, B, or C?

1. English class starts at 10:30
2. It's 1:30.
3. Manuel eats breakfast at 8:15 A.M.

LISTENING II
(Track 12) Page 16. Listen to the question and three answers.
What is the correct answer: A, B, or C?

4. When do you go to school?
   A. That's early!
   B. I go to school from 1 to 4.
   C. You're really busy!

5. Fatima gets home at 8:30 at night.
   A. I work from Tuesday to Thursday.
   B. It's 8:30.
   C. That's late!

6. What time is it?
   A. At 9:00.
   B. It's 4:30.
   C. It's from 2:00 to 4:00.

(Track 13) Page 16. Listen to the conversation. Then listen to the question and three answers.
What is the correct answer: A, B, or C?

7. **M:** When do you work?
   F: I work on Monday and Tuesday.

   When does the woman work?
   A. from Monday to Friday
   B. on Monday and Tuesday
   C. on Monday and Thursday

8. **M:** What time is the break at school?
   F: It's from 9:30 to 10:00 in the morning.

   When is the break?
   A. It's from 9:30 to 10:00.
   B. It's at 8:30.
   C. It's at 10:00.

9. **F:** What time is the class over?
   M: It's over at 12:00 in the afternoon.

   When is the class over?
   A. at 12:00 P.M.
   B. at 2:00 A.M.
   C. at 12:00 A.M.

Unit 4 Test Answer Key

ANSWERS	LESSON/PAGE	OBJECTIVE
1 (A) (B) (C) (D)	1/p. 63	Identify family members
2 (A) (B) (C) (D)	5/p. 70	Say and write dates
3 (A) (B) (C) (D)	1/p. 63	Identify family members
4 (A) (B) (C) (D)	2/p. 64	Say who is in a family
5 (A) (B) (C) (D)	4/p. 69	Identify months and ordinal numbers
6 (A) (B) (C) (D)	4/p. 68	Identify months and ordinal numbers
7 (A) (B) (C) (D)	2/p. 64	Say who is in a family
8 (A) (B) (C) (D)	3/p. 67	Talk about household chores
9 (A) (B) (C) (D)	2/p. 65	Singular/plural
10 (A) (B) (C) (D)	3/p. 67	Questions with *who*
11 (A) (B) (C) (D)	2/p. 65	Singular/plural
12 (A) (B) (C) (D)	3/p. 67	Questions with *who*
13 (A) (B) (C) (D)	2/p. 65	Singular/plural
14 (A) (B) (C) (D)	4/p. 68	Identify months and ordinal numbers
15 (A) (B) (C) (D)	2/p. 64	Identify family members
16 (A) (B) (C) (D)	2/p. 64	Identify family members
17 (A) (B) (C) (D)	3/p. 66	Identify household chores
18 (A) (B) (C) (D)	6/p. 72	Fill out a form
19 (A) (B) (C) (D)	6/p. 72	Fill out a form
20 (A) (B) (C) (D)	6/p. 72	Fill out a form
21 (A) (B) (C) (D)	6/p. 72	Fill out a form
22 (A) (B) (C) (D)		Read for details
23 (A) (B) (C) (D)		Read for details
24 (A) (B) (C) (D)		Read for details
25 (A) (B) (C) (D)		Read for details

Please see reverse for test audio script.

Unit 4 Test Audio Script

(Track 14) Page 23. Look at the pictures and listen.
What is the correct answer: A, B, or C?

1. That's my husband.
2. Today's date is October 9, 2008.

LISTENING II
(Track 15) Page 24. Listen to the question and three answers.
What is the correct answer: A, B, or C?

3. Who's that?
   A. September 7, 2007.
   B. No, I don't.
   C. That's my mother.

4. Do you have any children?
   A. That's nice.
   B. Yes. I have three daughters.
   C. My grandmother makes dinner.

5. When is your birthday?
   A. April 12.
   B. I vacuum.
   C. I have two sisters.

(Track 16) Page 24. Listen to the conversations. Then listen to the question and three answers.
What is the correct answer: A, B, or C?

6. **F:** Tom, what's your favorite month?
   M: August.

   What is the man's favorite month?
   A. October
   B. November
   C. August

7. **F:** Do you have any sons or daughters?
   M: Yes. I have one son and one daughter.

   Does the man have children?
   A. Yes. He has two sons.
   B. No.
   C. Yes. He has one son and one daughter.

8. **M:** Tessa, who washes the dishes at your house?
   F: My mother.

   Who washes dishes?
   A. Tessa's mother
   B. Tessa's brother
   C. Tessa's sister

Unit 5 Test Answer Key

ANSWERS	LESSON/PAGE	OBJECTIVE
1 Ⓐ Ⓑ **Ⓒ** Ⓓ	4/p. 87	Ask for and give prices
2 Ⓐ **Ⓑ** Ⓒ Ⓓ	2/p. 83	Make change with U.S. bills
3 Ⓐ **Ⓑ** Ⓒ Ⓓ	2/p. 83	Make change with U.S. bills
4 **Ⓐ** Ⓑ Ⓒ Ⓓ	4/p. 87	Ask for and give prices
5 **Ⓐ** Ⓑ Ⓒ Ⓓ	3/p. 85	Ask for drugstore items
6 **Ⓐ** Ⓑ Ⓒ Ⓓ	2/p. 83	Make change with U.S. bills
7 Ⓐ Ⓑ **Ⓒ** Ⓓ	3/p. 85	Ask for drugstore items
8 Ⓐ **Ⓑ** Ⓒ Ⓓ	4/p. 87	Ask for and give prices
9 **Ⓐ** Ⓑ Ⓒ Ⓓ	3/p. 85	*Where is/Where are*
10 Ⓐ Ⓑ **Ⓒ** Ⓓ	3/p. 85	*Where is/Where are*
11 Ⓐ **Ⓑ** Ⓒ Ⓓ	3/p. 85	*Where is/Where are*
12 Ⓐ **Ⓑ** Ⓒ Ⓓ	3/p. 85	*Where is/Where are*
13 Ⓐ **Ⓑ** Ⓒ Ⓓ	3/p. 85	*Where is/Where are*
14 **Ⓐ** Ⓑ Ⓒ Ⓓ	1/p. 80	Identify U.S. coins
15 Ⓐ Ⓑ Ⓒ **Ⓓ**	1/p. 80	Identify U.S. coins
16 Ⓐ **Ⓑ** Ⓒ Ⓓ	3/p. 84	Identify drugstore items
17 Ⓐ Ⓑ Ⓒ **Ⓓ**	3/p. 84	Identify drugstore items
18 Ⓐ Ⓑ **Ⓒ** Ⓓ	5/p. 88	Read a receipt
19 Ⓐ **Ⓑ** Ⓒ Ⓓ	5/p. 88	Read a receipt
20 Ⓐ Ⓑ Ⓒ **Ⓓ**	5/p. 89	Write a check
21 Ⓐ Ⓑ **Ⓒ** Ⓓ	5/p. 89	Write a check
22 Ⓐ **Ⓑ** Ⓒ Ⓓ		Read for details
23 Ⓐ Ⓑ Ⓒ **Ⓓ**		Read for details
24 **Ⓐ** Ⓑ Ⓒ Ⓓ		Read for details
25 Ⓐ Ⓑ **Ⓒ** Ⓓ		Read for details

Please see reverse for test audio script.

Unit 5 Test Audio Script

LISTENING I
(Track 17) Page 31. Look at the pictures and listen.
What is the correct answer: A, B, or C?

1 The aspirin is five dollars and twenty nine cents.

2. Do you have change for a five?

LISTENING II
(Track 18) Page 32. Listen to the question and three answers.
What is the correct answer: A, B, or C?

3. Do you have change for a twenty?
    A. Thanks.
    B. Yes, I have two tens.
    C. Excuse me.

4. Is shampoo on sale?
    A. Yes, it is.
    B. The toothpaste is $2.99.
    C. Yes, I have three quarters.

5. Where are the razor blades?
    A. They're $4.99.
    B. Aisle 2.
    C. How much are they?

(Track 19) Page 32. Listen to the conversation. Then listen to the question and three answers.
What is the correct answer: A, B, or C?

6. F: Do you have change for a ten?
    M: Yes, I have ten singles.

    How much money does the woman have?
    A. ten dollars
    B. five dollars
    C. one dollar

7. M: Where is the deodorant?
    F: Aisle 8.

    What is in Aisle 8?
    A. razor blades
    B. soap
    C. deodorant

8. F: Is soap on sale?
    M: Yes, it is. It's $3.49.

    How much is the soap?
    A. $2.49
    B. $3.49
    C. $4.39

Unit 6 Test Answer Key

	ANSWERS	LESSON/PAGE	OBJECTIVE
1	Ⓐ Ⓑ Ⓒ Ⓓ	2/p. 98	Talk about likes and dislikes
2	Ⓐ Ⓑ Ⓒ Ⓓ	1/p. 97	Talk about quantities of food
3	Ⓐ Ⓑ Ⓒ Ⓓ	1/p. 97	Talk about quantities of food
4	Ⓐ Ⓑ Ⓒ Ⓓ	4/p. 103	Talk about shopping for food
5	Ⓐ Ⓑ Ⓒ Ⓓ	6/p. 106	Read a menu and order a meal
6	Ⓐ Ⓑ Ⓒ Ⓓ	3/p. 101	Talk about likes and dislikes
7	Ⓐ Ⓑ Ⓒ Ⓓ	6/p. 106	Read a menu and order a meal
8	Ⓐ Ⓑ Ⓒ Ⓓ	1/p. 97	Talk about shopping for food
9	Ⓐ Ⓑ Ⓒ Ⓓ	2/p. 99	*Like/Don't like*
10	Ⓐ Ⓑ Ⓒ Ⓓ	2/p. 99	*Like/Don't like*
11	Ⓐ Ⓑ Ⓒ Ⓓ	3/p. 101	*Likes/Doesn't like*
12	Ⓐ Ⓑ Ⓒ Ⓓ	3/p. 101	*Likes/Doesn't like*
13	Ⓐ Ⓑ Ⓒ Ⓓ	2/p. 99	*Like/Don't like*
14	Ⓐ Ⓑ Ⓒ Ⓓ	3/p. 100	Identify fruit
15	Ⓐ Ⓑ Ⓒ Ⓓ	1/p. 96	Identify vegetables
16	Ⓐ Ⓑ Ⓒ Ⓓ	6/p. 106	Identify food on a menu
17	Ⓐ Ⓑ Ⓒ Ⓓ	6/p. 106	Identify food on a menu
18	Ⓐ Ⓑ Ⓒ Ⓓ	4/p. 102	Identify containers and amounts
19	Ⓐ Ⓑ Ⓒ Ⓓ	4/p. 102	Identify containers and amounts
20	Ⓐ Ⓑ Ⓒ Ⓓ	5/p. 104	Read ads/write a list
21	Ⓐ Ⓑ Ⓒ Ⓓ	5/p. 104	Read ads/write a list
22	Ⓐ Ⓑ Ⓒ Ⓓ	5/p. 104	Read ads/write a list
23	Ⓐ Ⓑ Ⓒ Ⓓ		Read for details
24	Ⓐ Ⓑ Ⓒ Ⓓ		Read for details
25	Ⓐ Ⓑ Ⓒ Ⓓ		Read for details

Please see reverse for test audio script.

Unit 6 Test Audio Script

LISTENING I
(Track 20) Page 39. Look at the pictures and listen.
What is the correct answer: A, B, or C?

1. I don't like cucumbers.

2. We have oranges.

LISTENING II
(Track 21) Page 40. Listen to the question and three answers.
What is the correct answer: A, B, or C?

3. Do we need carrots?
   A. Yes.
   B. I'm at the store.
   C. I don't like mushrooms.

4. What do we need from the store?
   A. No, thanks.
   B. A loaf of bread.
   C. Yes, I like carrots.

(Track 22) Page 40. Listen to the conversations. Then listen to the question and three answers.
What is the correct answer: A, B, or C?

5. **F:** Can I take your order?
   M: Yes. I'd like coffee and cake.

   What does the man want?
   A. tea and pancakes
   B. iced tea and cake
   C. coffee and cake

6. **M:** Does your son like fruit?
   F: Yes, he likes grapes. He doesn't like pears.

   What does the woman's son like?
   A. pears
   B. grapes and pears
   C. grapes

7. **M:** Are you ready to order?
   F: Yes, I'd like a green salad.

   What does the woman want?
   A. a green salad
   B. a baked potato
   C. a fruit salad

8. **F:** I'm at the store. Do we need avocados?
   M: Yes. Get avocados and tomatoes, please.

   What does the man want from the store?
   A. potatoes
   B. tomatoes and onions
   C. avocados and tomatoes

Unit 7 Test Answer Key

	ANSWERS	LESSON/PAGE	OBJECTIVE
1	(A) B C D	1/p. 115	Identify rooms in a home
2	A B (C) D	3/p. 119	Identify furniture and appliances
3	A (B) C D	4/p. 121	Ask for and give an address
4	A B (C) D	4/p. 121	Ask about an apartment
5	A B (C) D	2/p. 116	Ask about an apartment
6	(A) B C D	3/p. 119	Identify furniture and appliances
7	A B (C) D	2/p. 116	Ask about an apartment
8	(A) B C D	4/p. 121	Ask about an apartment
9	A (B) C D	2/p. 117	*There is/There are*
10	(A) B C D	2/p. 117	*There is/There are*
11	A B (C) D	3/p. 119	*Is there /Are there*
12	(A) B C D	3/p. 119	*Is there /Are there*
13	A B (C) D	3/p. 119	*Is there /Are there*
14	A B C (D)	1/p. 114	Identify rooms in a house
15	(A) B C D	1/p. 114	Identify rooms in a house
16	(A) B C D	3/p. 118	Identify furniture and appliances
17	A B C (D)	3/p. 118	Identify furniture and appliances
18	A (B) C D	5/p. 122	Address an envelope
19	A B (C) D	5/p. 122	Address an envelope
20	A B (C) D	5/p. 122	Address an envelope
21	A (B) C D	5/p. 122	Address an envelope
22	A B (C) D		Read for details
23	A (B) C D		Read for details
24	A B C (D)		Read for details
25	A B C (D)		Read for details

Please see reverse for test audio script.

Unit 7 Test Audio Script

LISTENING I
(Track 23) Page 47. Look at the pictures and listen.
What is the correct answer: A, B, or C?

1. The apartment has a living room.
2. There is a stove in the apartment.

LISTENING II
(Track 24) Page 48. Listen to the question and three answers.
What is the correct answer: A, B, or C?

3. What's the address?
   A. I have a new apartment.
   B. It's 155 North Blake Street.
   C. It has one bedroom.

4. I'm looking for an apartment.
   A. It's $775 a month.
   B. There's a modern bathroom.
   C. There's an apartment for rent on my block.

5. Can you tell me about the apartment?
   A. It's 1440 Carnation Street.
   B. No, there aren't.
   C. There is a small kitchen.

(Track 25) Page 48. Listen to the conversation. Then listen to the question and three answers.
What is the correct answer: A, B, or C?

6. M: Is there a dishwasher in the apartment?
   F: Yes, there is.

   What is in the apartment?
   A. a dishwasher
   B. a washing machine
   C. a dryer

7. F: What's the apartment like?
   M: It has a living room, a kitchen, and two bedrooms.

   What does the man's apartment have?
   A. a living room, a kitchen, and one bedroom
   B. a dining room, a kitchen, and two bedrooms
   C. a living room, a kitchen, and two bedrooms

8. F: How much is the rent for your apartment?
   M: It's $895 a month.

   How much is the man's rent?
   A. $895 a month
   B. $795 a month
   C. $805 a month

Unit 8 Test Answer Key

	ANSWERS	LESSON/PAGE	OBJECTIVE
1	Ⓐ **Ⓑ** Ⓒ Ⓓ	2/p. 132	Ask about clothing size
2	**Ⓐ** Ⓑ Ⓒ Ⓓ	1/p. 131	Talk about clothes and shoes
3	**Ⓐ** Ⓑ Ⓒ Ⓓ	2/p. 132	Ask about clothing size
4	Ⓐ Ⓑ **Ⓒ** Ⓓ	2/p. 135	Say what someone is wearing
5	**Ⓐ** Ⓑ Ⓒ Ⓓ	4/p. 136	Return clothes and say the problem
6	Ⓐ Ⓑ **Ⓒ** Ⓓ	2/p. 132	Ask about clothing size
7	**Ⓐ** Ⓑ Ⓒ Ⓓ	4/p. 136	Return clothes and say the problem
8	Ⓐ Ⓑ **Ⓒ** Ⓓ	2/p. 133	*This/That/These/Those*
9	**Ⓐ** Ⓑ Ⓒ Ⓓ	2/p. 133	*This/That/These/Those*
10	Ⓐ **Ⓑ** Ⓒ Ⓓ	3/p. 135	Adjective + noun
11	Ⓐ **Ⓑ** Ⓒ Ⓓ	2/p. 133	*This/That/These/Those*
12	Ⓐ Ⓑ **Ⓒ** Ⓓ	3/p. 135	Adjective + noun
13	Ⓐ **Ⓑ** Ⓒ Ⓓ	4/p. 136	Problems with clothes
14	Ⓐ Ⓑ Ⓒ **Ⓓ**	4/p. 136	Problems with clothes
15	Ⓐ Ⓑ Ⓒ **Ⓓ**	1/p. 130	Identify clothes and shoes
16	Ⓐ **Ⓑ** Ⓒ Ⓓ	1/p. 130	Identify clothes and shoes
17	Ⓐ Ⓑ Ⓒ **Ⓓ**	3/p. 134	Identify colors
18	Ⓐ Ⓑ **Ⓒ** Ⓓ	3/p. 134	Identify colors
19	Ⓐ Ⓑ Ⓒ **Ⓓ**	5/p. 138	Read a store ad
20	Ⓐ Ⓑ **Ⓒ** Ⓓ	5/p. 138	Read a store ad
21	Ⓐ **Ⓑ** Ⓒ Ⓓ	5/p. 138	Read a store ad
22	Ⓐ **Ⓑ** Ⓒ Ⓓ	5/p. 138	Read a store ad
23	Ⓐ Ⓑ **Ⓒ** Ⓓ		Read for details
24	Ⓐ Ⓑ Ⓒ **Ⓓ**		Read for details
25	Ⓐ Ⓑ **Ⓒ** Ⓓ		Read for details

Please see reverse for test audio script.

Unit 8 Test Audio Script

LISTENING I
(Track 26) Page 54. Look at the pictures and listen.
What is the correct answer: A, B, or C?

1. Do you have this shirt in a medium?
2. I need new pants.

LISTENING II
(Track 27) Page 55. Listen to the question and three answers.
What is the correct answer: A, B, or C?

3. Do you have these pants in a size 10?
   A. No, I'm sorry, we don't.
   B. OK, I need new shoes.
   C. Can I help you?

4. Is Carmen here?
   A. OK. Thanks.
   B. It is too big.
   C. Yes. She's over there. She's wearing a purple shirt.

5. I need to return some shoes.
   A. What's the problem?
   B. He's wearing a green jacket.
   C. Here's my receipt.

(Track 28) Page 55. Listen to the conversation. Then listen to the question and three answers.
What is the correct answer: A, B, and C?

6. **M:** Do you have this jacket in a large?
   F: Yes, we do.

   What does the man want?
   A. a large shirt
   B. a small jacket
   C. a large jacket

7. **F:** What's the problem?
   M: The shirt is too long.

   What is the man's problem?
   A. His shirt is too long.
   B. His T-shirt is too short.
   C. His shirt is too small.

Unit 9 Test Answer Key

ANSWERS	LESSON/PAGE	OBJECTIVE
1 Ⓐ Ⓑ **C** Ⓓ	3/p. 151	Ask what someone is doing now
2 Ⓐ Ⓑ **C** Ⓓ	1/p. 147	Talk about free-time activities
3 Ⓐ **B** Ⓒ Ⓓ	2/p. 148	Say what someone is doing
4 Ⓐ Ⓑ **C** Ⓓ	2/p. 148	Say what someone is doing now
5 **A** Ⓑ Ⓒ Ⓓ	3/p. 151	Say what someone is doing now
6 Ⓐ **B** Ⓒ Ⓓ	1/p. 147	Talk about free-time activities
7 Ⓐ Ⓑ **C** Ⓓ	3/p. 151	Say what someone is doing now
8 **A** Ⓑ Ⓒ Ⓓ	4/p. 153	Say what someone is doing now
9 Ⓐ **B** Ⓒ Ⓓ	5/p. 154	Listen and write a message
10 **A** Ⓑ Ⓒ Ⓓ	5/p. 154	Listen and write a message
11 **A** Ⓑ Ⓒ Ⓓ	2/p. 149	Present continuous
12 Ⓐ Ⓑ **C** Ⓓ	3/p. 151	Present continuous, *yes/no* questions
13 **A** Ⓑ Ⓒ Ⓓ	3/p. 151	Present continuous, *yes/no* questions
14 **A** Ⓑ Ⓒ Ⓓ	3/p. 151	Present continuous, *yes/no* questions
15 Ⓐ **B** Ⓒ Ⓓ	4/p. 153	Present continuous negative
16 Ⓐ Ⓑ **C** Ⓓ	1/p. 146	Identify free-time activities
17 Ⓐ Ⓑ Ⓒ **D**	1/p. 146	Identify free-time activities
18 Ⓐ **B** Ⓒ Ⓓ	1/p. 146	Identify free-time activities
19 Ⓐ Ⓑ **C** Ⓓ	3/p. 150	Identify household chores
20 Ⓐ **B** Ⓒ Ⓓ	5/p. 154	Listen and write a message
21 Ⓐ Ⓑ **C** Ⓓ	5/p. 154	Listen and write a message
22 Ⓐ Ⓑ **C** Ⓓ		Read for details
23 Ⓐ Ⓑ Ⓒ **D**		Read for details
24 **A** Ⓑ Ⓒ Ⓓ		Read for details
25 Ⓐ **B** Ⓒ Ⓓ		Read for details

Please see reverse for test audio script.

Unit 9 Test Audio Script

LISTENING I
(Track 29) Page 63. Look at the pictures and listen.
What is the correct answer: A, B, or C?

1. Are you doing the laundry?
2. I read the newspaper.

LISTENING II
(Track 30) Page 64. Listen to the question and three answers.
What is the correct answer: A, B, or C?

3. Are you busy?
   A. Bye.
   B. Yes. I'm exercising.
   C. No problem.

4. Can I call you later?
   A. How often?
   B. I play the guitar.
   C. No problem. Bye.

5. Is Rashid using e-mail?
   A. No, he isn't.
   B. I'll see him later.
   C. He does homework.

(Track 31) Page 64. Listen to the conversation. Then listen to the question and three answers.
What is the correct answer: A, B, or C?

6. M: Do you go to the movies?
   F: Yes, I do.

   What does the woman do?
   A. She uses e-mail.
   B. She goes to the movies.
   C. She listens to music.

7. F: Is Laura visiting friends?
   M: No. She's watching TV.

   What is Laura doing?
   A. She's talking on the phone.
   B. She's visiting friends.
   C. She's watching TV.

8. F: Where is Oscar? Is he taking a break?
   M: No. He isn't taking a break. He's working on the computer.

   What is Oscar doing?
   A. He's working on the computer.
   B. He's looking for something.
   C. He's taking a break.

LIFE SKILLS I
(Track 32) Page 65. Look at the pictures and listen. What is the correct answer: A, B, or C?

9. M: Hi. This is Howard Smith. Can I speak to Mr. Wong?
   F: Mr. Wong is not here. Can I take a message?

10. M: Dr. Flaggman is not here. Can I take a message?
    F: Yes. I can't come to my appointment today. My daughter is sick.

Unit 10 Test Answer Key

ANSWERS	LESSON/PAGE	OBJECTIVE
1 Ⓐ Ⓑ **C** Ⓓ	1/p. 163	Talk about places in the community
2 **A** Ⓑ Ⓒ Ⓓ	3/p. 167	Talk about types of transportation
3 Ⓐ **B** Ⓒ Ⓓ	2/p. 165	Give directions
4 **A** Ⓑ Ⓒ Ⓓ	1/p. 163	Talk about places in the community
5 Ⓐ **B** Ⓒ Ⓓ	3/p. 167	Talk about types of transportation
6 Ⓐ Ⓑ **C** Ⓓ	3/p. 167	Talk about where someone is
7 Ⓐ **B** Ⓒ Ⓓ	3/p. 167	Talk about types of transportation
8 Ⓐ Ⓑ **C** Ⓓ	4/p. 169	Ask for and give directions
9 Ⓐ **B** Ⓒ Ⓓ	2/p. 165	*Between/Across from*
10 Ⓐ Ⓑ **C** Ⓓ	2/p. 165	*Between/Across from*
11 Ⓐ **B** Ⓒ Ⓓ	2/p. 165	*Between/Across from*
12 Ⓐ Ⓑ **C** Ⓓ	2/p. 165	*Between/Across from*
13 Ⓐ **B** Ⓒ Ⓓ	2/p. 165	*Between/Across from*
14 **A** Ⓑ Ⓒ Ⓓ	1/p. 162	Identify places in the community
15 Ⓐ Ⓑ **C** Ⓓ	1/p. 162	Identify places in the community
16 **A** Ⓑ Ⓒ Ⓓ	3/p. 166	Identify types of transportation
17 Ⓐ Ⓑ **C** Ⓓ	3/p. 166	Identify types of transportation
18 **A** Ⓑ Ⓒ Ⓓ	4/p. 168	Ask for and give directions
19 Ⓐ **B** Ⓒ Ⓓ	4/p. 168	Ask for and give directions
20 Ⓐ Ⓑ Ⓒ **D**	4/p. 168	Ask for and give directions
21 Ⓐ Ⓑ **C** Ⓓ	5/p. 170	Read traffic signs
22 Ⓐ Ⓑ Ⓒ **D**	5/p. 170	Read traffic signs
23 Ⓐ Ⓑ **C** Ⓓ		Read for details
24 Ⓐ Ⓑ **C** Ⓓ		Read for details
25 Ⓐ Ⓑ Ⓒ **D**		Read for details

Please see reverse for test audio script.

Unit 10 Test Audio Script

LISTENING I
(Track 33) Page 71. Look at the pictures and listen.
What is the correct answer: A, B, or C?

1. Excuse me. Is there a post office near here?

2. I ride a bike to school.

LISTENING II
(Track 34) Page 72. Listen to the question and three answers.
What is the correct answer: A, B, or C?

3. Where is the gas station?
   A. Take the subway.
   B. On the corner of First Street and Main Street.
   C. I'm going to my English class.

4. Is there a park near here?
   A. Yes. It's across from the library.
   B. How do you get to school?
   C. Thanks a lot!

5. How does Tom get to work?
   A. Go straight.
   B. He walks.
   C. Turn left at White Street.

(Track 35) Page 72. Listen to the conversation. Then listen to the question and three answers.
What is the correct answer: A, B, or C?

6. **M:** Where are you going?
   F: I'm going to the ATM.

   Where is the woman going?
   A. to the subway
   B. to the school
   C. to the ATM

7. **M:** How do your children get to school?
   F: They take a train.

   How do the woman's children get to school?
   A. They take a taxi.
   B. They take a train.
   C. They take a ferry.

LIFE SKILLS I
(Track 36) Page 73. Look at the pictures and listen. What is the correct answer: A, B, or C?

8. **M:** Where's the computer store?
   F: Turn right on Bank Street.

Unit 11 Test Answer Key

ANSWERS	LESSON/PAGE	OBJECTIVE
1 (A) **(B)** (C) (D)	3/p. 183	Talk about common health problems
2 **(A)** (B) (C) (D)	2/p. 180	Follow medical instructions
3 (A) (B) **(C)** (D)	1/p. 179	Talk about common health problems
4 (A) **(B)** (C) (D)	1/p. 179	Make an appointment
5 **(A)** (B) (C) (D)	3/p. 183	Talk about common health problems
6 (A) **(B)** (C) (D)	4/p. 185	Call 911 for emergencies
7 **(A)** (B) (C) (D)	3/p. 183	Talk about common health problems
8 (A) (B) **(C)** (D)	4/p. 185	Call 911 for emergencies
9 (A) (B) **(C)** (D)	3/p. 183	*Should*
10 (A) **(B)** (C) (D)	3/p. 183	*Should*
11 **(A)** (B) (C) (D)	2/p. 180	Imperatives
12 (A) **(B)** (C) (D)	2/p. 180	Imperatives
13 (A) (B) **(C)** (D)	3/p. 183	*Should*
14 (A) (B) (C) **(D)**	2/p. 180	Follow medical instructions
15 **(A)** (B) (C) (D)	2/p. 180	Follow medical instructions
16 **(A)** (B) (C) (D)	1/p. 178	Identify parts of the body
17 (A) (B) (C) **(D)**	1/p. 178	Identify parts of the body
18 **(A)** (B) (C) (D)	5/p. 186	Identify medicines
19 (A) (B) (C) **(D)**	5/p. 186	Identify medicines
20 (A) (B) **(C)** (D)	5/p. 186	Identify medicines
21 **(A)** (B) (C) (D)	5/p. 187	Read a medicine label
22 (A) (B) **(C)** (D)	5/p. 187	Read a medicine label
23 (A) (B) (C) **(D)**		Read for details
24 (A) (B) **(C)** (D)		Read for details
25 (A) **(B)** (C) (D)		Read for details

Please see reverse for test audio script.

Unit 11 Test Audio Script

LISTENING I
(Track 37) Page 81. Look at the pictures and listen.
What is the correct answer: A, B, or C?

1. He has a cough.
2. Please sit on the table.

LISTENING II
(Track 38) Page 82. Listen to the question and three answers.
What is the correct answer: A, B, or C?

3. What's the problem?
   A. You should drink lots of liquids.
   B. Look straight ahead.
   C. My knee hurts.

4. Can she come in for an appointment at 2:00?
   A. My head hurts.
   B. Yes, she can.
   C. I have an appointment.

5. What's the matter?
   A. I have a stomachache.
   B. Get well soon!
   C. Open your mouth.

(Track 39) Page 82. Listen to the conversation. Then listen to the question and three answers.
What is the correct answer: A, B, or C?

6. **M:** Where are you?
   F: 1133 Main Street in Garden City.

   Where is the woman?
   A. She's across the street.
   B. She's on Main Street.
   C. She's on Garden Street.

7. **F:** I have the flu.
   M: You should get a lot of rest.

   What does the woman need?
   A. a lot of rest
   B. a lot of liquids
   C. aspirin

8. **M:** What's the emergency?
   F: My father is having a heart attack.

   What's the matter?
   A. There was a car accident.
   B. The woman's father has a backache.
   C. The woman's father is having a heart attack.

Unit 12 Test Answer Key

ANSWERS	LESSON/PAGE	OBJECTIVE
1 Ⓐ Ⓑ **Ⓒ** Ⓓ	2/p. 197	Talk about jobs
2 Ⓐ **Ⓑ** Ⓒ Ⓓ	2/p. 197	Talk about jobs
3 Ⓐ Ⓑ **Ⓒ** Ⓓ	1/p. 195	Talk about jobs
4 Ⓐ **Ⓑ** Ⓒ Ⓓ	2/p. 197	Ask about someone's job
5 **Ⓐ** Ⓑ Ⓒ Ⓓ	3/p. 199	Talk about job skills
6 Ⓐ **Ⓑ** Ⓒ Ⓓ	1/p. 195	Talk about jobs
7 **Ⓐ** Ⓑ Ⓒ Ⓓ	2/p. 197	Ask about someone's job
8 Ⓐ Ⓑ **Ⓒ** Ⓓ	4/p. 200	Apply for a job
9 Ⓐ Ⓑ **Ⓒ** Ⓓ	2/p. 197	*Where does/Where do*
10 Ⓐ Ⓑ **Ⓒ** Ⓓ	4/p. 201	*Can: Yes/No* questions and short answers
11 Ⓐ **Ⓑ** Ⓒ Ⓓ	2/p. 197	*Where does/Where do*
12 Ⓐ Ⓑ **Ⓒ** Ⓓ	4/p. 201	*Can: Yes/No* questions and short answers
13 Ⓐ **Ⓑ** Ⓒ Ⓓ	4/p. 201	*Can: Yes/No* questions and short answers
14 Ⓐ Ⓑ **Ⓒ** Ⓓ	3/p. 198	Identify job skills
15 Ⓐ **Ⓑ** Ⓒ Ⓓ	3/p. 198	Identify job skills
16 Ⓐ **Ⓑ** Ⓒ Ⓓ	2/p. 196	Identify jobs
17 Ⓐ Ⓑ **Ⓒ** Ⓓ	2/p. 196	Identify jobs
18 Ⓐ Ⓑ **Ⓒ** Ⓓ	5/p. 202	Read a job ad
19 Ⓐ **Ⓑ** Ⓒ Ⓓ	5/p. 202	Read a job ad
20 **Ⓐ** Ⓑ Ⓒ Ⓓ	5/p. 202	Read a job ad
21 Ⓐ **Ⓑ** Ⓒ Ⓓ	5/p. 202	Read a job ad
22 Ⓐ Ⓑ Ⓒ **Ⓓ**	5/p. 202	Read a job ad
23 Ⓐ **Ⓑ** Ⓒ Ⓓ		Read for details
24 Ⓐ Ⓑ **Ⓒ** Ⓓ		Read for details
25 Ⓐ Ⓑ Ⓒ **Ⓓ**		Read for details

Please see reverse for test audio script.

Unit 12 Test Audio Script

LISTENING I
(Track 40) Page 89. Look at the pictures and listen.
What is the correct answer: A, B, or C?

1. She's a bus driver.
2. He's a security guard.

LISTENING II
(Track 41) Page 90. Listen to the question and three answers.
What is the correct answer: A, B, or C?

3. What do you do?
   A. Let's get coffee.
   B. I can't. I have to go to work.
   C. I'm a construction worker.

4. Where does she work?
   A. That's Brenda.
   B. She works at Family Restaurant.
   C. She's a nurse.

5. What are your job skills?
   A. I use a computer.
   B. I'd like to apply for a job.
   C. I work at Longview Hospital.

6. **M:** What do you do?
   F: I'm a teacher's assistant.

   What is the woman's job?
   A. She works in a café.
   B. She's a teacher's assistant.
   C. She's a sales assistant.

7. **F:** Where does your brother work?
   M: He works at Shopwell Supermarket.

   Where does the man's brother work?
   A. at a supermarket
   B. at a drugstore
   C. at a restaurant

8. **M:** I can fix cars.
   F: OK. Please fill out the application for the mechanic's job.

   What can the man do?
   A. build houses
   B. help sick people
   C. fix cars

To use the *Future* **Exam***View*® *Assessment Suite*, your computer must meet or exceed the following requirements:

For Windows®*:*
- Intel Pentium® II 120 MHz or compatible processor
- Microsoft Windows® 2000/XP/Vista

For Macintosh®*:*
- Power PC® 120 MHz or higher processor
- Mac OS X (10.2 or later)

Both:
- 100 MB of available hard drive space
- 128 MB of available RAM (256 MB recommended)
- Monitor capable of displaying 16-bit color with 800 x 600 resolution
- Internet connection to access test-hosting features, and for Content Update Feature
- CD-ROM Drive

These instructions are for **Exam***View Test Generator* version 6. If you have an earlier version of **Exam***View* installed on your computer, it will automatically be replaced by this version when you install it. You can then create all your new tests in this version. If you open an existing test or question bank created with the earlier version, it will automatically be updated.

For Windows®*:*
1. Close all other programs before you begin the installation.
2. Insert the **Exam***View* disc into the CD-ROM drive of your computer.
3. You may be prompted by the computer to open the disc. If this doesn't happen, open **My Computer**.
4. Double-click on the CD-ROM drive icon.

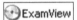

5. Double click on the TO THE TEACHER document in order to read it. This document will instruct you in the best practices to use the *Future* **Exam***View Assessment Suite* products. The document will also provide instructions for using the listening portions of the *Future* **Exam***View* tests.
6. After closing the TO THE TEACHER document, double click on the SETUP file and follow the instructions on the screen.
7. When the installation is complete, remove the **Exam***View* disc from the CD-ROM drive of your computer.

For Macintosh®*:*
1. Close all other programs before you begin the installation.
2. Insert the **Exam***View* disc into the CD-ROM drive of your computer.
3. Double-click on the **Exam***View* icon that appears on the desktop.
4. Double click on the TO THE TEACHER document in order to read it. This document will instruct you in the best practices to use the *Future* **Exam***View Assessment Suite* products. The document will also provide instructions for using the listening portions of the *Future* **Exam***View* tests.
5. After closing the TO THE TEACHER document, double click on the **Exam***View* installer icon and follow the instructions on the screen.
6. When installation is complete, remove the **Exam***View* disc from the CD-ROM drive of your computer.

ISBN-13: 978-0-13-240929-2
ISBN-10: 0-13-240929-1